DDISON-WESLEY

WESTERN CANADIAN EDITION

pplied Mathematics 12

Kerr

PROJECT BOOK

Robert Alexander
Mathematics Teacher
and Consultant
Richmond Hill, Ontario

Cam Bennet
Dauphin Regional
Comprehensive
Secondary School
Dauphin, Manitoba

Garry Davis
Saskatoon Public Board
of Education
Saskatoon, Saskatchewan

Carol Besteck Hope
Elmwood High School
Winnipeg, Manitoba

Terry Kaminski
Grand Centre High School
Cold Lake, Alberta

Jim Nakamoto
Sir Winston Churchill
Secondary School
Vancouver, British Columbia

Brent Richards
Crocus Plains Regional
Secondary School
Brandon, Manitoba

David Sufrin
Ballenas Secondary School
Parksville, British Columbia

Paul Williams
Red Deer College
Red Deer, Alberta

Elizabeth Wood
Calgary Board of Education
Calgary, Alberta

Rick Wunderlich
Shuswap Junior
Secondary School
Salmon Arm, British Columbia

Leanne Zorn
Mount Boucherie
Secondary School
Kelowna, British Columbia

Addison Wesley

Toronto

PUBLISHER
Claire Burnett

MANAGING EDITOR
Enid Haley

SENIOR CONSULTING EDITOR
Lesley Haynes

PRODUCT MANAGER
Reid McAlpine

DEVELOPMENTAL EDITOR
Anna-Maria Garnham

DESIGN/PRODUCTION/ART DIRECTION
Pronk&Associates

ISBN: 0-201-39598-3

This book contains recycled product and is acid free.

Printed and bound in Canada

2 3 4 5 – TCP – 05 04 03 02

Addison Wesley

Toronto

CONTENTS

Applied Mathematics 12 Project Book

Introduction

Welcome to *Applied Mathematics 12 Project Book*

Each project in this Project Book gives you an opportunity to apply new mathematics. Having 24 projects means you can choose projects that interest you.

Organization

Here is how a typical project works.

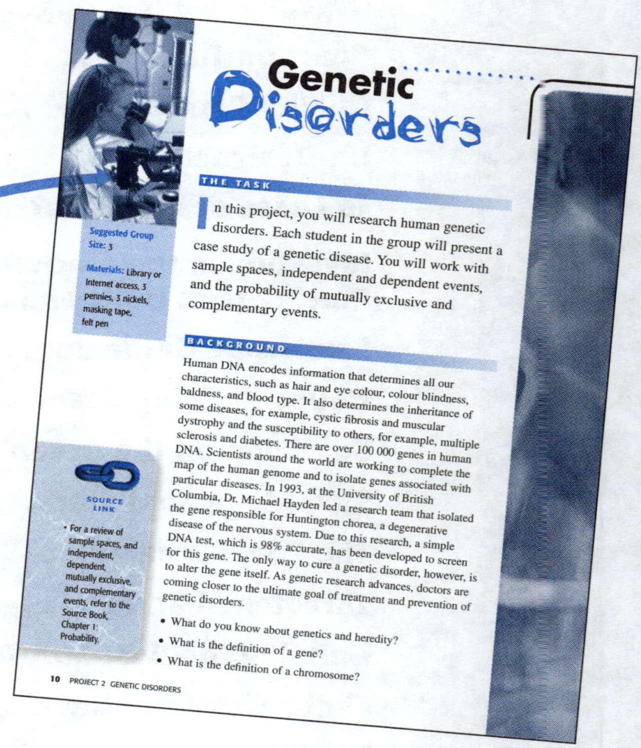

Genetic Disorders

THE TASK

In this project, you will research human genetic disorders. Each student in the group will present a case study of a genetic disease. You will work with sample spaces, independent and dependent events, and the probability of mutually exclusive and complementary events.

Suggested Group Size: 3

Materials: Library or Internet access, 3 pennies, 3 nickels, masking tape, felt pen

BACKGROUND

Human DNA encodes information that determines all our characteristics, such as hair and eye colour, colour blindness, baldness, and blood type. It also determines the inheritance of some diseases, for example, cystic fibrosis and muscular dystrophy and the susceptibility to others, for example, multiple sclerosis and diabetes. There are over 100 000 genes in human DNA. Scientists around the world are working to complete the map of the human genome and to isolate genes associated with particular diseases. In 1993, at the University of British Columbia, Dr. Michael Hayden led a research team that isolated the gene responsible for Huntington chorea, a degenerative disease of the nervous system. Due to this research, a simple DNA test, which is 98% accurate, has been developed to screen for this gene. The only way to cure a genetic disorder, however, is to alter the gene itself. As genetic research advances, doctors are coming closer to the ultimate goal of treatment and prevention of genetic disorders.

- What do you know about genetics and heredity?
- What is the definition of a gene?
- What is the definition of a chromosome?

SOURCE LINK

- For a review of sample spaces, and independent, dependent, mutually exclusive, and complementary events, refer to the Source Book, Chapter 1: Probability.

10 PROJECT 2 GENETIC DISORDERS

- **The Task** explains the purpose of the project.
- **Materials** lists the supplies you need to complete the project. You may have ideas for additional or alternative supplies.
- **Background** provides some interesting facts about the topic or sets up a possible scenario for your project.
- **Source Link** points you to required skills in the Source Book, if you need them.

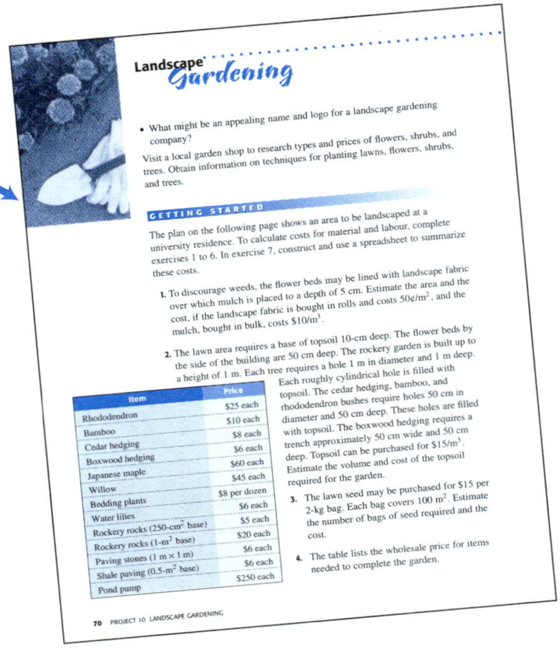

Landscape Gardening

- What might be an appealing name and logo for a landscape gardening company?

Visit a local garden shop to research types and prices of flowers, shrubs, and trees. Obtain information on techniques for planting lawns, flowers, shrubs, and trees.

GETTING STARTED

The plan on the following page shows an area to be landscaped at a university residence. To calculate costs for material and labour, complete exercises 1 to 6. In exercise 7, construct and use a spreadsheet to summarize these costs.

1. To discourage weeds, the flower beds may be lined with landscape fabric over which mulch is placed to a depth of 5 cm. Estimate the area and the cost, if the landscape fabric is bought in rolls and costs 50¢/m^2, and the mulch, bought in bulk, costs \$10/m^3.

2. The lawn area requires a base of topsoil 10-cm deep. The flower beds by the side of the building are 50 cm deep. The rockery garden is built up to a height of 1 m. Each tree requires a hole 1 m in diameter and 1 m deep. Each roughly cylindrical hole is filled with topsoil. The cedar hedging, bamboo, and rhododendron bushes require holes 50 cm in diameter and 50 cm deep. These holes are filled with topsoil. The boxwood hedging requires a trench approximately 50 cm wide and 50 cm deep. Topsoil can be purchased for \$15/m^3. Estimate the volume and cost of the topsoil required for the garden.

Item	Price
Rhododendron	\$25 each
Bamboo	\$10 each
Cedar hedging	\$8 each
Boxwood hedging	\$6 each
Japanese maple	\$60 each
Willow	\$45 each
Bedding plants	\$8 per dozen
Water lilies	\$6 each
Rockery rocks (250-cm^2 base)	\$5 each
Rockery rocks (1-m^2 base)	\$20 each
Paving stones (1 m × 1 m)	\$6 each
Shale paving (0.5-m^2 base)	\$6 each
Pond pump	\$250 each

3. The lawn seed may be purchased for \$15 per 2-kg bag. Each bag covers 100 m^2. Estimate the number of bags of seed required and the cost.

4. The table lists the wholesale price for items needed to complete the garden.

70 PROJECT 10 LANDSCAPE GARDENING

- **Getting Started** leads you to explore some of the basic mathematical concepts underlying the project application.
- **Project Presentation** lets you pursue a variety of extensions of the work done in Getting Started, and suggests ways to present your project report.
- **Career Opportunities** describes how the mathematical skills of the project relate to careers.

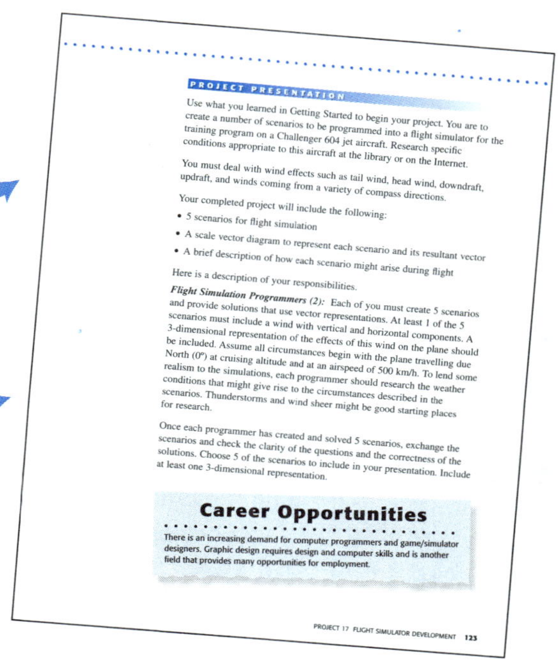

PROJECT PRESENTATION

Use what you learned in Getting Started to begin your project. You are to create a number of scenarios to be programmed into a flight simulator for the training program on a Challenger 604 jet aircraft. Research specific conditions appropriate to this aircraft at the library or on the Internet.

You must deal with wind effects such as tail wind, head wind, downdraft, updraft, and winds coming from a variety of compass directions.

Your completed project will include the following:

- 5 scenarios for flight simulation
- A scale vector diagram to represent each scenario and its resultant vector
- A brief description of how each scenario might arise during flight

Here is a description of your responsibilities.

Flight Simulation Programmers (2): Each of you must create 5 scenarios and provide solutions that use vector representations. At least 1 of the 5 scenarios must include a wind with vertical and horizontal components. A 3-dimensional representation of the effects of this wind on the plane should be included. Assume all circumstances begin with the plane travelling due North (0°) at cruising altitude and at an airspeed of 500 km/h. To lend some realism to the simulations, each programmer should research the weather conditions that might give rise to the circumstances described in the scenarios. Thunderstorms and wind sheer might be good starting places for research.

Once each programmer has created and solved 5 scenarios, exchange the scenarios and check the clarity of the questions and the correctness of the solutions. Choose 5 of the scenarios to include in your presentation. Include at least one 3-dimensional representation.

Career Opportunities

There is an increasing demand for computer programmers and game/simulator designers. Graphic design requires design and computer skills and is another field that provides many opportunities for employment.

PROJECT 17 FLIGHT SIMULATOR DEVELOPMENT 123

Working in Groups

Each project gives a suggested group size. In the workplace, one of the most important traits employers look for is team spirit. Companies rely on their employees to work together efficiently and well. That is one reason many projects in this book are designed for groups. Follow these guidelines so that your team works efficiently and well.

TRACKING POLLUTION

THE TASK

In this project, you will examine the possibility that radioactive wastes travel via ocean currents and investigate possible effects of radioactive wastes on living things. You will use vector analysis to track the movement of pollutants in a model case.

Suggested Group Size: 2

Materials: Grid paper, Internet access (optional)

BACKGROUND

Over the years, the world's oceans, rivers, and lakes have been used as chemical dumps. Water pollution in the form of mercury poisoning caused horrific birth defects in Japan. Drums of radioactive wastes have been dumped into the oceans from ships. Buried wastes have leached from containers into waterways and supplies of drinking water. Contamination of water supplies by a virulent form of *E. coli* has been linked to deaths in Ontario. All these situations are cause for concern; pollution control agreements and careful monitoring are needed to avoid similar problems.

Because natural bodies of water are dynamic moving masses, chemical pollutants can travel from their place of origin to places where their damage can be profound. Oceanographers and marine biologists are often called on to trace the origins of pollutants in an attempt to reduce or prevent damage to people and the environment in general.

In this project, you will study environments in which water moves as the result of currents or river flow. You will use vector analysis to predict the path of materials placed in such environments.

SOURCE LINK

- To review vector analysis, refer to the Source Book, Chapter 7: Vectors. For help with exponential equations and radioactive decay, see the Student Reference.

124 PROJECT 18 TRACKING POLLUTION

- Select strategies together.
- Respect each other. Accept different ideas on how to approach a problem.
- Practise patience and allow everybody to have a say. If everyone in the group talks at the same time, no one listens or hears.

All of you have something unique to contribute to the group. Work together so that the group can produce a plan for action and a finished piece of work at the end.

In business, a company succeeds on the strength of its teams. When you work in a group, you will all be assessed together. Everyone will benefit if you work well as a team.

Multiple Strategies and Solutions

The projects in this book are open ended. There are many valid strategies and solutions.

Your solution will probably differ from that of any other group. You should expect this and remember that all solutions are just that — one answer to the problem. All can be equally appropriate.

We wish you every success!

Project Requirements

Project Name	Skills and Concepts Covered in the Source Book (Chapter)
NiDi	1
Genetic Disorders	1
Creating and Selling Rustic Twig Furniture	2
Organizing a Meeting	2
Reaction Time	3
Quality Control	3
Un-Designer Jeans	3
To Lease or Purchase?	4
Investing in the Stock Market – Playing with Bulls and Bears!	4
Landscape Gardening	4
House Building Costs	4
Surviving on the Ocean's Shore	5
Sun, Moon, and Stars	5
The Ponzi Scheme	6
Threatened and Endangered Species	6
Building the Best Soft-Drink Container	6
Flight Simulator Development	7
Tracking Pollution	7
Training a Robot	7
Shelving Systems	
Toy Design	
Cable Pathways	
Ergonomic Design	
Designing a Storage Tank	

To cover the Grade 12 Applied Mathematics curriculum **you should complete:**

- **Building the Best Soft-Drink Container**

Outcomes **A9-1, A9-2, A9-3 and A9-4** are addressed **solely** in these projects.

- **Landscape Gardening**
- **Toy Design**
- **Ergonomic Design**
- **Shelving Systems**
- **Cable Pathways**
- **Designing a Storage Tank**

NiDi

Suggested Group Size: 2

Materials: One penny, 7 nickels, 7 dice

Optional: Cardboard tubes, boxboard or Bristol board, scissors and tape, interactive geometry software, a protractor, paper clips, straight pins

THE TASK

In this project you will investigate the game of NiDi. Play the game several times to develop strategies for winning. Study the probabilities in the game to develop an optimal strategy, and modify the game so that a different strategy is needed. You will work with the fundamental counting principle, sample spaces, independent and dependent events, and probabilities of mutually exclusive and complementary events.

BACKGROUND

Many games, and many real-life events, depend on chance. Decision making often involves an understanding of the likelihood that an event will occur and/or the relationship between events. What does it mean in a weather forecast if the POP (probability of precipitation) is 90%? What does a POP of 0% mean?

What are the chances that events will occur together? How often are there dual failures in a system? For example, if a monitor board is cracked and causes intermittent failure, how likely is it that the power cord is loose and also a cause of intermittent failure? The areas of warranties and insurance depend on statistical probabilities.

Some events are linked; one depends on the others. Other events are independent. Still other events are mutually exclusive; if one event occurs, the other cannot.

SOURCE LINK

- To review probability, look in the Source Book, Chapter 1: Probability.

NiDi

Explain why the pairs of events below are dependent, independent, or mutually exclusive.

- You attend a football game. Your neighbours mow their lawn.
- Today is payday. You buy a new CD.
- You have a date for Friday evening. You are asked to work the Friday late shift.
- You flip a coin; the result is heads. You roll a die; the result is 4.
- You roll a pair of dice; the red die shows 2. The total of dice is 11.
- You win the school raffle. You win the hockey pool draw in the same week.

GETTING STARTED

The Rules of NiDi

Players take turns and record the scores for each round.

Materials: 1 penny, 7 nickels, 7 dice

The Play

Flip the penny.

Flip as many nickels as you wish, all at once.

Roll the same number of dice as the number of nickels you flipped.

The Score

For every nickel that shows the same face as the penny, score 5 points.

If *any* 2 dice show the same face, cancel your score for the turn.

1. Play one 5-round game with 2 to 4 players and calculate each person's total score for the game. High score wins.

2. Play 10 games in which players use from 1 to 7 nickels and dice. Record the scores for each number of nickels used in a table similar to Table 1. What strategies are best? How many nickels and dice give the highest overall score? Can you prove your claim?

Table 1 Scores at NiDi

# of NiDi	Scores										Average Score
1											
2											
3											
4											
5											
6											
7											

Collect the results from other groups and add them to your table. Calculate the average score for each of 1, 2, ..., or 7 nickels. (With large amounts of data, a histogram for each NiDi number may show an interesting and useful pattern.) Revise your strategy if you see a different trend with larger amounts of data.

3. What is the largest number of dice you should attempt to roll? Why?

4. NiDi is a simple game with a lot of depth. In the game, there are three factors: Penny, Nickels, and Dice.

a) What role does each play in the system?

b) Which is the most important factor in the game?

c) Are any of the factors limiting?

5. The data in Table 1, obtained from many games, indicates an observed probability. A closer look at the events in the game can provide a theoretical probability. There are two sides to this: the potential score and the probability of actually scoring. To set up Table 2, the NiDi Theoretical Probability Table, complete the exercises below.

a) The potential score is determined by the outcome of the nickels matching the penny. (For simplicity, assume the penny turns up heads.) The average potential score can be determined by averaging the scores of all the possible outcomes. If 1 nickel is flipped, there are only two possible scores: 0 or 5. Explain why this is so. What is the average of these two outcomes?

NiDi

Table 2 NiDi Theoretical Probability Table

# of NiDi	Average Score Potential	Probability of Scoring	Average Score Expected
1			
2			
3			
4			
5			
6			
7			

b) Assume the penny turns up heads. If 2 nickels are flipped, how many outcomes are there? List them all. (Consider the nickels to be labelled A and B.) What are the potential scores for each outcome and what is the average score for all outcomes?

c) Create a list of all the possible outcomes (a sample space) and the scores when 3, 4, 5, 6, and 7 nickels are used. Continue to assume the penny turned up heads. What is the average potential score in each case? Can you explain any patterns in the data? Use your answers from parts a, b, and c to complete column 2 of Table 2.

6. The probability of scoring depends on the roll of the dice. In order to score, there must not be any doubles; all the dice must be different. Use the combined probabilities of complementary events. The first die can turn up any way, thus the probability of scoring with 1 die is $\frac{6}{6} = 1$. With 2 dice, the first can turn up any way, but the second must not match the first. How many acceptable ways can the second die turn up? What is the probability that the second die will not match? Since these events are independent, the combined probability that both will occur is the product of the individual probabilities: $\frac{6}{6} \times \frac{?}{6} =$___.

A third die cannot match either of the other two. How many acceptable ways can it turn up? What is the probability of this? What is the probability of scoring with 3 dice? Use this reasoning to find the probability of scoring with 1 to 7 dice and record your findings in column 3 of Table 2.

7. The average score expected on any turn will be the average score potential × probability of scoring. Record these values in column 4 of Table 2. From this table, what strategy would you suggest gives the best results in a game of NiDi? Does this agree with the strategy you devised in exercise 3?

PROJECT PRESENTATION

Use what you learned in Getting Started to begin your project. Adapt the game of NiDi by adjusting the game pieces used. Substitute n-sided dice for normal dice and adjust the probabilities and strategy. Methods of making a set of n-dice, or suitable alternatives, are provided at the end of this project.

Your completed project will contain the following items.

- Data tables and/or graphs of the results of all NiDi games played by your group
- A compilation of data gathered from other groups
- A discussion of the roles and importance of the penny, the nickels, and the dice in the game of NiDi
- A variant of NiDi obtained by adjusting the game pieces used
- A discussion of winning strategies (with evidence) for the standard game of NiDi and for your group's variant
- Complete Theoretical Probability Tables for the standard game of NiDi and for your group's variant
- A set of materials or equipment to allow your variant of NiDi to be played by other groups
- A discussion of why the best strategy may not always be the winning strategy

Here are detailed descriptions of each person's responsibilities.

Theoretician: Your role is to choose a number, n, to use for n-dice (dice with n sides). You will prepare sample spaces and complete a NiDi Theoretical Probability Table for your n-dice game. Finally, you will determine and explain the best strategy for winning under the new conditions.

Games Analyst: You will be responsible for organizing the materials for your group to prepare a set of n-dice. After you prepare the n-dice, arrange a game of your variant of NiDi against another group and coordinate the scorekeeping.

NiDi

Statistician: Your job will be to gather, record, and display data from all games of the variant of NiDi devised by your group. You will also analyze the data to assist the Theoretician to devise the best strategy for winning your new form of NiDi.

All group members will assist with the final preparation and presentation of the project.

Career Opportunities

An understanding of probability is essential to many areas of business, science, sport, and health planning. The interpretation of probability is central to occupations such as weather forecaster, insurance analyst, systems planner, and financial advisor.

Making a Set of *n*-dice

1. Choose any number, n, to make a set of n-dice (dice with n sides).

2. Collect several cardboard tubes.

3. Use an interactive geometry software package, such as *The Geometer's Sketchpad* to make an n-gon.

a) Create a circle equal in size to the outside of the cardboard tube.

b) Make a tangent to the circle at some point on the circle and mark the centre of the circle as a point of rotation by double clicking on it.

End plate for 7-sided die

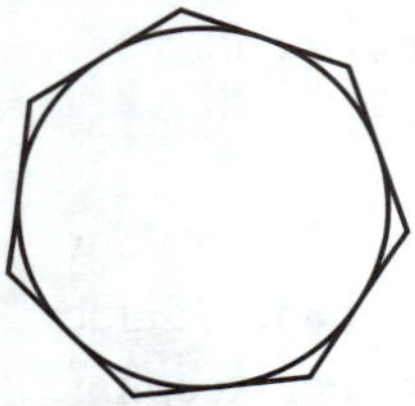

c) Select the tangent and rotate (under **Transform** menu) by $\frac{360^\circ}{n}$. Repeat this rotation on the new tangent until you have n tangents and are back to the original position.

d) Create and select points at the intersections of the tangents around the circle. Construct these segments to make an n-gon.

e) Hide all the tangents and print your page.

4. Cut out the n-gon and use it as a template to make more identical n-gons from boxboard. Tape an n-gon to each end of the cardboard tubes. Make sure that the edges of the n-gons match.

5. Measure the edge, e, of an n-gon and the length, l, of a tube with the ends on.

6. Cut out n strips of boxboard for each tube. Each strip will have dimensions $e \times l$.

7. Tape these strips to make a set of n-gon tubes that can be numbered and used as rolling n-dice. Make several dice more than the number needed for your predicted best strategy.

Spinners

A set of spinners is a simple alternative to the n-dice.

1. Draw or create a large circle and draw a radius.

2. Rotate the radius by $\frac{360^\circ}{n}$ and repeat until you have a circle with n equal sectors.

3. Number each sector. Use a partially straightened paper clip to make a spinner. Spin it about a pencil or a pin at the centre of the circle.

4. Make a set of spinners to use instead of n-dice.

7 sector spinner

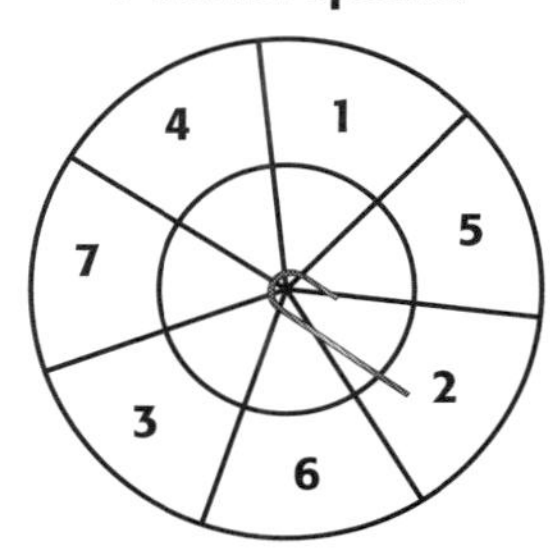

Random Numbers

The TI-83 random number generator will provide results equivalent to rolling any number of n-sided dice.

1. For example, to simulate a roll of 7 ten-sided dice you press [MATH] [◄] **5 1** [,] **10** [,] **7** [)] [STO►] [2nd] **1** [ENTER]. Your roll is placed in L1 and can be viewed there.

2. To help you to spot doubles, use Sort A. Press [2nd] [STAT] [►] **1** [2nd] **1** [)] [ENTER]. This will sort the list shown in L1 in ascending order. To view this list press [2nd] **1**.

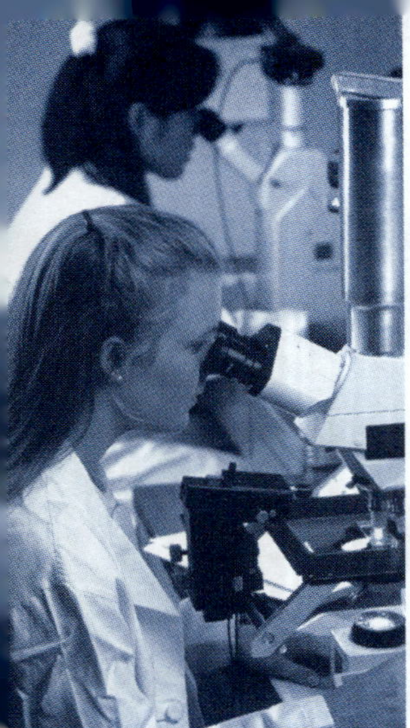

Genetic Disorders

Suggested Group Size: 3

Materials: Library or Internet access, 3 pennies, 3 nickels, masking tape, felt pen

THE TASK

In this project, you will research human genetic disorders. Each student in the group will present a case study of a genetic disease. You will work with sample spaces, independent and dependent events, and the probability of mutually exclusive and complementary events.

BACKGROUND

Human DNA encodes information that determines all our characteristics, such as hair and eye colour, colour blindness, baldness, and blood type. It also determines the inheritance of some diseases, for example, cystic fibrosis and muscular dystrophy and the susceptibility to others, for example, multiple sclerosis and diabetes. There are over 100 000 genes in human DNA. Scientists around the world are working to complete the map of the human genome and to isolate genes associated with particular diseases. In 1993, at the University of British Columbia, Dr. Michael Hayden led a research team that isolated the gene responsible for Huntington chorea, a degenerative disease of the nervous system. Due to this research, a simple DNA test, which is 98% accurate, has been developed to screen for this gene. The only way to cure a genetic disorder, however, is to alter the gene itself. As genetic research advances, doctors are coming closer to the ultimate goal of treatment and prevention of genetic disorders.

- What do you know about genetics and heredity?
- What is the definition of a gene?
- What is the definition of a chromosome?

SOURCE LINK

- For a review of sample spaces, and independent, dependent, mutually exclusive, and complementary events, refer to the Source Book, Chapter 1: Probability.

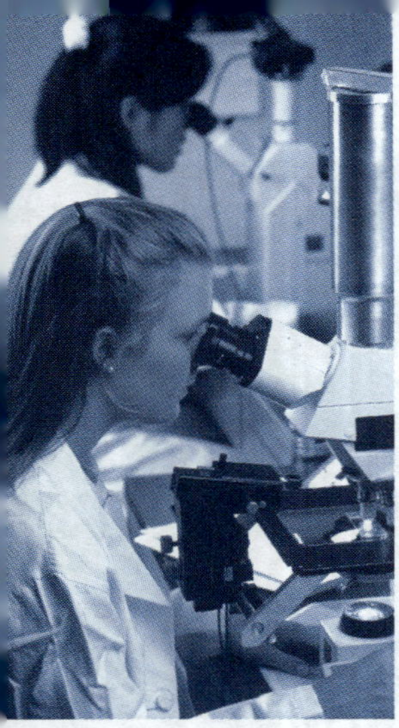

Genetic Disorders

- What genetic diseases have you heard about?
- List examples of dominant and recessive traits in humans.
- Can you roll your tongue?

GETTING STARTED

You will need to understand some of the basic ideas and terms involved in the study of genetics. Read the examples below and answer the questions. Refer to a biology textbook or ask your teacher if you need help.

Part A: The Individual

Your ability, or inability, to roll your tongue is determined by certain genes passed on to you by your parents. There are two forms (alleles) of the gene that determines tongue-rolling ability. These are labelled **R** and **r**. **R** represents the allele responsible for "**R**oller," and **r** represents the allele responsible for "non-**r**oller."

The pair **R** and **r** is called a *genotype*. There are three different possibilities for the genotypes associated with tongue rolling. These are **RR**, **Rr**, and **rr**. (It is a convention to put the capital letter to the left of the small letter.) The capital letter **R** refers to the allele that is *dominant* (in this case **R**oller) and the small letter **r** refers to the allele that is *recessive* (in this case non-**r**oller). "Dominant" means that if a person's genotype has *at least one* capital **R** in it, the person is a **R**oller. So **RR** and **Rr** produce **R**ollers because the **R** dominates the **r**. "Recessive" means that if the person's genotype has two **r**s in it the person is a non-roller; thus **rr** is a non-**r**oller. *Phenotype* is the term used to describe the appearance of the trait (that is, what is observable).

Due to meiosis, a biological process in which the alleles segregate, there is a 50–50 chance that a sperm will contain one of the two alleles of the male's genotype, and there is a 50–50 chance that an egg will contain one of the two alleles of the female's genotype. The chart below summarizes these ideas.

Genotype (pair of alleles)	Phenotype (appearance)	Sperm/Egg May Contain
RR	**R**oller	**R** or **R**
Rr	**R**oller	**R** or **r**
rr	Non-**r**oller	**r** or **r**

The possibilities for the genotype and phenotype of offspring from a mating of a non-**r**oller male with genotype **rr**, and a **R**oller female, with genotype **Rr**, can be summarized in a Punnett Square.

The Punnett Square below is the sample space for the results of the mating.

		Female	
		R	**r**
Male	**r**	**Rr** **R**oller	**rr** Non-**r**oller
	r	**Rr** **R**oller	**rr** Non-**r**oller

The phenotype probabilities (**R**oller or non-**r**oller) are:

Probability of **R**oller, P(**R**oller) $= \frac{2}{4} = \frac{1}{2}$

Probability of non-**r**oller, P(non-**r**oller) $= \frac{2}{4} = \frac{1}{2}$

1. List the genotypes of all possible mating pairs for the tongue-rolling trait. For each pair, draw the associated Punnett Square and record the probabilities that their offspring will be **R**ollers or non-**r**ollers. Keep these results for later use.

2. Investigate how the theoretical probabilities for the offspring of different mating pairs compare with the experimental probabilities obtained when you toss coins in a simulation experiment. Set up 3 pennies to represent the possible male genotypes, **RR**, **Rr**, and **rr**, and 3 nickels to represent the possible female genotypes **RR**, **Rr**, and **rr**. Attach a label for **R** or **r** to each side of each coin.

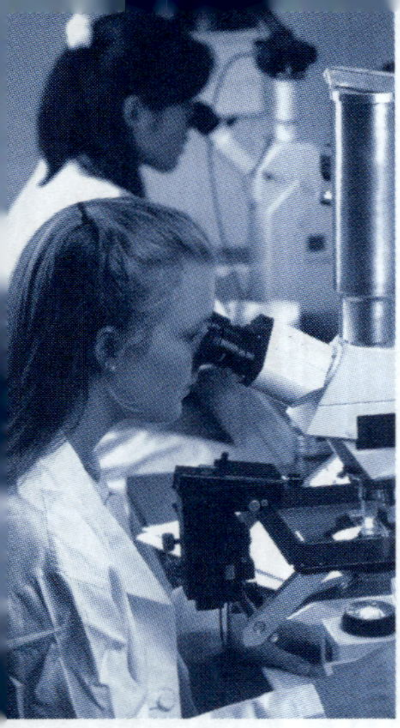

Genetic Disorders

Toss the coins in pairs: (1 penny and 1 nickel). For each of the mating pairs indicated below, toss the coins 100 times. Record the number of times the coins come up **RR**, **Rr**, or **rr** in a table similar to the one below. Record the number of **R**ollers and non-**r**ollers. Convert your data into percents.

Do the experiment for the following mating pairs:

i) Male **Rr** and female **Rr**

ii) Male **Rr** and female **rr**

iii) Male **RR** and female **RR**

iv) Male **rr** and female **rr**

MATING PAIR (GENOTYPES) ________ and ________

Offspring Genotypes and Phenotypes	RR	Rr	rr	ROLLER	NON-ROLLER
TALLY / 100					
PERCENT PROBABILITY					

a) Why is it unnecessary to toss the coins for the pairs in parts iii and iv?

b) Compare the probabilities from the experiments with the theoretical probabilities obtained in exercise 1.

c) What assumptions are made in this investigation?

3. Punnett Squares can be applied to gender determination. The gender of a human depends upon the gender chromosomes, designated X and Y. A female always has 2 X chromosomes, and a male always has an X and a Y. A person with an XX pair is female, and a person with an XY pair is male. There is a 50–50 chance that a sperm will contain one of the two gender chromosomes (X or Y), and a 50–50 chance that an egg will contain one of the two gender chromosomes (the first X or the second X). Copy and complete the Punnett Square below and state the probabilities that a child will be male, P(M), or female, P(F).

Female

Male		**X**	**X**
	X	XX Female	
	Y		

P(M) = P(F) =

4. It is possible to calculate the probabilities that combinations of traits will appear in offspring by using the Punnett Squares for more than one human trait.

   a) What is the probability that a child with male parent **Rr** and female parent **rr** will be a **R**oller?

   b) **H**anging earlobe (**H**) is dominant, while attac**h**ed earlobe (**h**) is recessive. What is the probability that a child with male parent **Hh** and female parent **Hh** will have an attac**h**ed earlobe?

   c) Are the probabilities in parts a and b dependent or independent?

   d) Calculate the probability that a child with male parent **Rr** and **Hh** and female parent **rr** and **Hh** will be a **R**oller with an attac**h**ed earlobe.

   e) What is the probability that a child of the mating described in part d is a male, non-**r**oller with a **H**anging earlobe?

5. A person is said to "carry" a recessive gene if their genotype has one dominant allele and one recessive allele. They will show the dominant trait even though they carry the recessive gene. For example, genotype **Hh** carries the recessive gene **h**.

   a) Determine the probability that a child of the mating described in exercise 4 part d carries the recessive gene **r**. What is the probability that the child carries the recessive gene **h**?

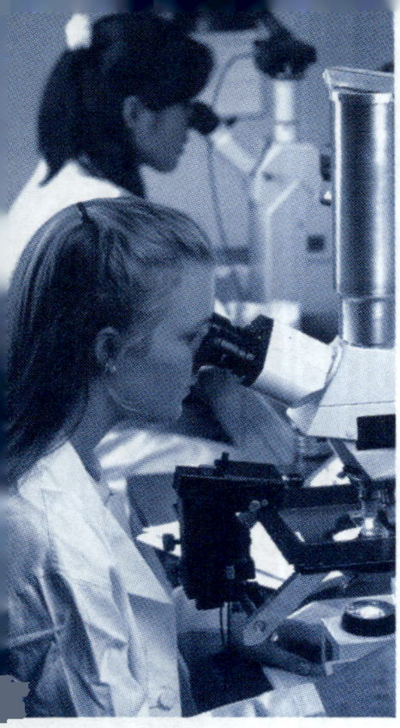

b) What is the probability that a child of this mating carries both recessive genes?

c) What is the probability that two of their children carry both recessive genes?

Sex-Linked (or X-Linked) Traits

Some traits, such as colour-blindness show a pattern of inheritance that is linked to gender. In this case, the gene determining colour blindness is located on the X chromosome. The alleles are **C** (non-colour blind, dominant) and **c** (colour blind, recessive). The convention is to write $\mathbf{X^C}$ for a chromosome with the dominant allele and $\mathbf{X^c}$ for a chromosome with the recessive allele. The Y chromosome does not contain information for this trait. The table below shows the phenotype (appearance) that results from each possible chromosome pair.

Chromosome Pair	Description (Phenotype)
$X^C X^C$	Non-colour-blind female
$X^C X^c$	Non-colour-blind female carrier
$X^c X^c$	Colour-blind female
$X^C Y$	Non-colour-blind male
$X^c Y$	Colour-blind male

Punnett Squares can be applied to the inheritance of X-linked genes.

6. Copy and complete the Punnett Square below for the mating of a female carrier ($\mathbf{X^C X^c}$) and a non-colour-blind male ($\mathbf{X^C Y}$).

State the probability that offspring of this mating will be:

a) a colour-blind male ($\mathbf{X^c Y}$). **b)** non-colour blind.

Female

Male	X^C	X^c
X^C		$X^C X^c$ Female carrier Non-colour blind
Y		

7. Set up a Punnett Square for the mating of a non-colour-blind female with genotype ($\mathbf{X^C X^C}$) with a colour-blind male ($\mathbf{X^c Y}$). State the probability of this mating producing a female carrier ($\mathbf{X^C X^c}$).

Part B: Human Populations

The genetic make-up of an individual is set, and potential combinations of their genes with those of their mate will not affect their own survival. However, over time, as individuals have children, and as these children in turn have children, the *gene pool* will change. It is important to note that the terms "dominant" and "recessive" do not refer to how common or rare the gene is in a given population. Recessive genes can sometimes be very prevalent, while dominant genes might be quite rare. It is also important to note that not all traits occur in equal proportions. Knowledge of the frequencies of various genes in a population can allow prediction of the probabilities of the occurrence of genetic disorders.

Two mathematicians, G.H. Hardy and W. Weinberg, working separately, developed a mathematical model that allows calculation of the frequency of genes in a population under certain conditions. Their model is as follows, where **A** and **a** are alleles of the gene for a typical human trait:

If p is the frequency (probability) of the dominant gene **A** in a given population, and q is the frequency (probability) of the recessive gene **a**, then

Frequency of **AA** $= p \times p = p^2$
Frequency of **aa** $= q \times q = q^2$
Frequency of **Aa** $= 2pq$
$p^2 + 2pq + q^2 = 1$
$p + q = 1$ (The sum of the probabilities of complementary events is 1.)

8. Consider the trait of tongue rolling. If a person is a **R**oller the genotype could be either **RR** or **Rr**, but it is not possible to know which by observation. If a person is a non-**r**oller, the genotype MUST be **rr**. Use this fact and the Hardy–Weinberg model to determine the frequencies of **RR** and **Rr**.

a) Suppose that in a given population 84% are **R**ollers. The frequency is thus 0.84. What percent are non-**r**ollers? What is the frequency of non-**r**ollers?

b) Set q^2 equal to the frequency found in part a and calculate the value of q.

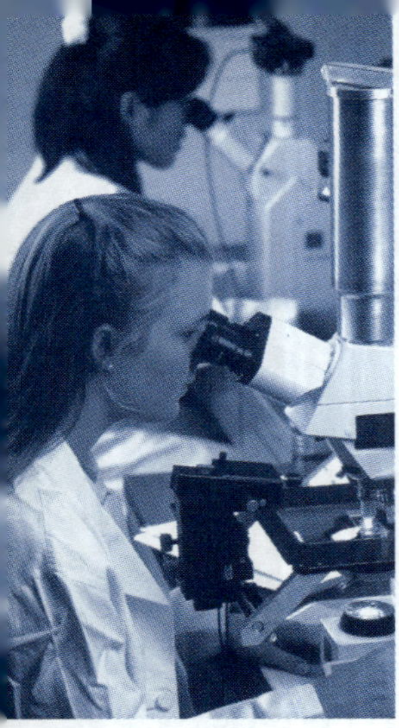

c) Use the fact that $p + q = 1$ to calculate p.

d) Use the values of p and q to determine p^2 and $2pq$.

e) Fill in the table below.

Genotype	Frequency
RR	
Rr	
rr	

f) In the population described above, what is the probability that a person will be a carrier of the recessive gene?

9. Suppose the dominant genetic trait of a **H**anging earlobe occurs in 9% of a population. Use the Hardy–Weinberg model to determine the following.

a) The frequency of attac**h**ed earlobes

b) The frequency of people who are carriers of the recessive gene **h**

10. Choose one observable dominant trait (for example, tongue **R**oller) and take a survey of 100 people. Try to sample 50 males and 50 females. Record the number who exhibit the trait, and the number who do not.

Use your data and the Hardy–Weinberg method to calculate the frequency of carriers of the recessive gene. Consider the results for males and for females. Does this trait appear to be sex-linked?

PROJECT PRESENTATION

Use what you learned in Getting Started to complete your project. Work as a team to prepare a report on 3 genetic disorders in humans.

The examples will show a) a recessive; b) a dominant; and c) an X-linked pattern of inheritance.

For each disorder, your presentation should include the following items.

- A description of the pattern of inheritance of the condition
- Punnett Squares for all possible matings and probabilities for the genotypes and phenotypes of offspring

- A description of the associated symptoms
- Information on any advances made in determination and treatment of the disorder
- The frequency of the disorder in the general population (where possible)
- A determination of the frequencies of non-sufferers and carriers, based on the Hardy–Weinberg method.

Here is a description of each person's responsibilities.

Researcher 1: Research and report on a *recessive disorder* in humans.

Researcher 2: Research and report on a *dominant disorder* in humans.

Researcher 3: Research and report on an *X-linked disorder* in humans.

Career Opportunities

An understanding of genetic disorders and patterns of inheritance is essential to health-care workers. Screening of newborns may identify a disorder that is treatable. Genetic counsellors provide education and support to families affected by genetic disorders. Ethicists must be aware of possible negative aspects of screening and counselling programs.

Suggested Group Size: 2

Materials: A number of small twigs and branches, a glue gun, garden clippers

Creating and Selling Rustic Twig Furniture

THE TASK

In this project, you will work in pairs to design and market twig furniture. You will use matrices to analyze the quantity of materials required, the costs for labour and materials, the markup and profit for each piece, and the monthly sales.

BACKGROUND

Rustic twig furniture was very popular in the second half of the nineteenth century throughout the United States and Canada, particularly in wilderness resorts and hotels, which catered to the growing "back-to-nature" tourism industry of the time. Local artisans marketed their work as souvenirs and small home-based businesses became profitable enterprises. In the last decade, there has been a resurgence of interest in twig furniture for use in houses and gardens. In addition to chairs and tables, a wide variety of items from planters and trellises to wine racks and lamp stands, may be made in the rustic twig style. The market is wide open for creative entrepreneurs to set up shop and sell their products.

- Have you seen any twig furniture in the houses or gardens of your family or friends? Describe the item(s).
- If you were to design a piece of twig furniture, what would you choose?
- Are there any stores in your community that sell twig furniture?
- Find a piece of twig furniture and look carefully at its construction.
- Research rustic twig furniture designs.

SOURCE LINK

- To review matrices, refer to the Source Book, Chapter 2: Matrices.

For help with the performance of matrix operations on the TI-83, refer to Utility 26.

Creating and Selling

Rustic Twig Furniture

GETTING STARTED

Twig furniture requires various different types, lengths, and diameters of branches and twigs. To create chairs, 1- to 2-inch diameter hardwood pieces are needed for the legs and frame, while $\frac{3}{4}$-inch diameter pliable pieces are needed for the seat and back. The wood has to be gathered and trimmed free of leaves and smaller twigs. It may then be cut into convenient lengths of approximately 3, 5, and 8 feet for transportation to the workshop for storage. When an item is constructed, branches will be cut to the exact lengths required and fastened together with nails or screws, or by cutting "tenon" joints, which are glued together. In the finishing stage, rough edges are sanded smooth and varnish or oil is applied.

Matrices are useful management tools for an entrepreneur who builds and sells rustic twig furniture. They may be used to keep track of the inventory of raw materials used, the hours of labour spent making the items, the monthly orders, and the costs and selling prices for each type of item. A number of matrices are outlined on following page. They relate to aspects of the operation of the business but do not have specific entries. The entries will be filled in and the operations performed as part of the Project Presentation.

1. Consider tables A and B below. In Table A, the 5 rows list different sizes and types of branches used and the columns list 3 types of furniture item made. A matrix can be created from Table A. **For this project, the convention will be to refer to matrix *A* as a 5 × 3 Size–Item matrix.** Create a 5 × 3 Size-Item matrix from Table A. Call this matrix *A*. The entries are for the number of each type of branch required for each item.

Table A

	Chair	Settee	Side Table
3-foot Hardwood			
5-foot Hardwood			
5-foot Pliable			
8-foot Pliable			
Total			

Table B shows entries for monthly orders for each item. Create a 3 × 4 **Item–Month** matrix from Table B. Call this matrix *B*. The entries are the monthly orders for each item.

Table B

	March	April	May	June
Chair				
Settee				
Side Table				

If you multiply matrices *A* and *B* to obtain a new matrix, *C*,

a) Will the order of multiplication be $A \times B$ or $B \times A$?

b) What are dimensions of the product?

c) Name the product matrix, *C*. Use the convention stated above.

d) What information do the entries of matrix *C* represent?

2. If it takes 1 h to collect sufficient branches for one item of furniture that requires 30 branches, how long does the collection process take per branch? If it takes approximately 4 h to construct an item that requires 30 branches, how long does the construction process take per branch? If it takes approximately 1 h to finish a furniture item with 30 branches, how long does the finishing process take per branch? Express your answers in hours correct to three decimal places.

Creating and Selling

Rustic Twig Furniture

3. Consider Table D. Create matrix *D* from Table D. The entries are the times, in hours, for each process.

Table D

	Chair	Settee	Side Table
Collection			
Construction			
Finishing			

a) Describe how you can use the information in the fifth row of matrix *A* together with the answers to exercise 2 to obtain the entries for the rows of matrix *D*?

b) What are the dimensions of matrix *D*?

c) Name matrix *D*. Use the convention stated above.

4. In Table E, the entries are the hourly labour costs for each process. Create matrix *E* from Table E. The entries are the rate per hour ($/h) for each process.

Table E

	Collection	Construction	Finishing
Labour Costs			

If matrix *D* and matrix *E* are multiplied to obtain matrix *F*,

a) Will the order of multiplication be $D \times E$ or $E \times D$?

b) What are the dimensions of the product matrix, *F*?

c) What information do the entries in matrix *F* represent?

5. Table G shows the costs for purchased materials (nails and varnish) for each type of furniture item. Create matrix *G*, a 1×3 matrix from Table G. The entries are the total costs for nails and varnish for each item.

Table G

	Chair	Settee	Side Table
Material Costs			

Another 1×3 matrix, *H*, is needed to show the total costs for materials and labour for each furniture item. How might this matrix be obtained from matrices *F* and *G*?

6. A 1×3 matrix, J, is needed to give the selling price for each item. If the selling price is obtained by applying a 25% markup on the total cost for each item, what operation must be performed on matrix H to obtain matrix J?

7. A 1×3 matrix, K, is needed to give the profit for each item of furniture. How is matrix K obtained from matrices H and J?

8. If matrix B and matrix K are multiplied to obtain matrix L,

   a) Will the order of multiplication be $B \times K$ or $K \times B$?

   b) What are the dimensions of the product matrix, L?

   c) What information is found in the entries of matrix L?

9. Examine the 3 items of twig furniture shown below to become familiar with the style. The materials lists give the numbers of components for a specific chair, table, or settee made in the rustic style. Use these lists to complete Table A.

Chair Materials

3-foot Hardwood	15
5-foot Hardwood	6
5-foot Pliable	14
8-foot Pliable	0
Galvanized Nails	40
Finishing Nails	60
Finishing Oil/Varnish	$\frac{1}{2}$ L

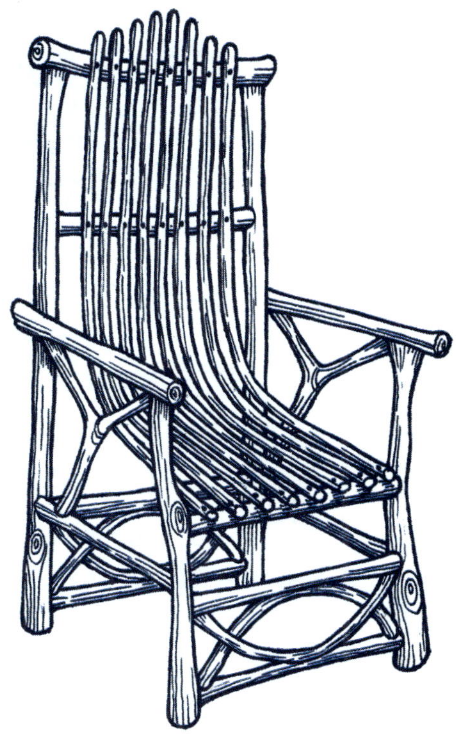

Creating and Selling

Rustic Twig Furniture

Side Table Materials

3-foot Hardwood	20
5-foot Hardwood	0
5-foot Pliable	4
8-foot Pliable	0
Galvanized Nails	20
Finishing Nails	60
Finishing Oil/Varnish	$\frac{1}{4}$ L

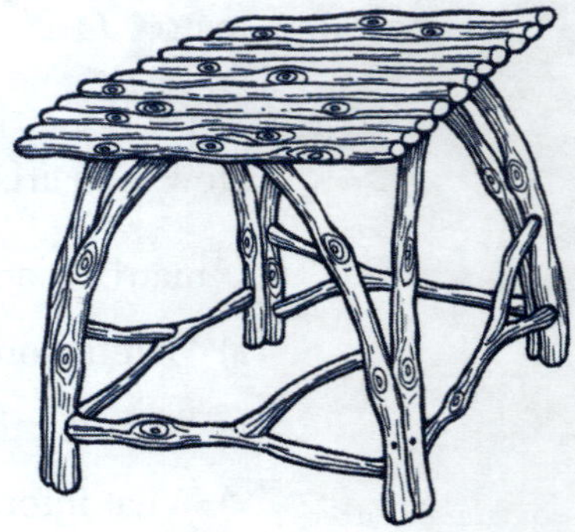

Settee Materials

3-foot Hardwood	15
5-foot Hardwood	5
5-foot Pliable	10
8-foot Pliable	3
Galvanized Nails	45
Finishing Nails	45
Finishing Oil/Varnish	$\frac{3}{4}$ L

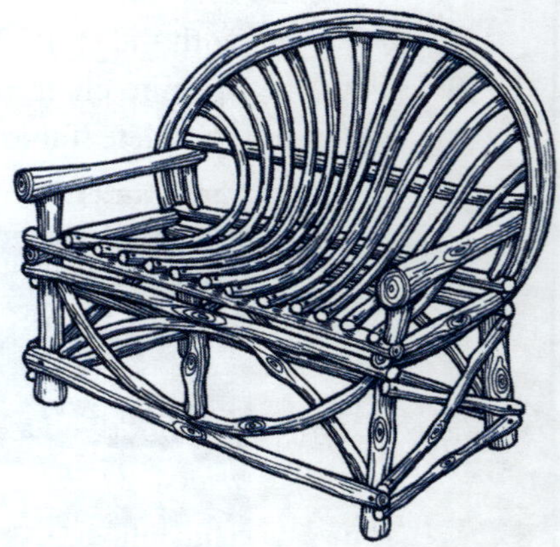

PROJECT PRESENTATION

Use what you learned in Getting Started to begin your project. Your completed project will consist of:

- A design for a piece of twig furniture that includes a list of the materials required
- A small model prototype made from twigs and small branches
- A series of completed matrices A to L that correspond to those outlined in Getting Started. These matrices analyze the quantity of materials required, the costs for labour and materials, the markup and profit for each piece, and the monthly sales. (Include your calculations.)

Here is a detailed description of each person's responsibilities.

Twig Furniture Artisan: Design and construct a small model of a piece of twig furniture. Describe the types and sizes of branches needed, the approximate number of nails or screws needed, and the amount of varnish or oil needed. Determine the approximate number of hours needed to construct the piece, from the collection of the branches through to the finishing process. Create your own estimates or use the figures in Getting Started as a guide. Choose two other pieces to be included in your stock. Research the costs for nails and varnish or oil to determine suitable entries for Table G. Decide upon an hourly wage for each of collection, construction, and finishing of each piece. Work with the Business Manager to provide entries for Tables A, D, E, and G and to create a matrix from each table.

Business Manager: Work with the Artisan to create Tables A, D, E, and G. Research probable monthly demands, or use your imagination to invent the numbers of monthly orders to provide entries for Table B. With the Artisan, produce matrices C, F, H, J, K, and L. Choose a percent markup on cost that will provide a good profit without making the pieces overpriced. Use the matrix feature of your graphing calculator to obtain your answers.

Career Opportunities

Project management skills from implementing a design to marketing a product are needed in all manufacturing industries. Inventory control, product costing, and profit projection have applications in manufacturing, wholesale, and retail business operations.

ORGANIZING a Meeting

Suggested Group Size: 3

Materials: A calculator capable of performing matrix operations, a computer with spreadsheet software, provincial road maps, and accommodation guides; Internet access (optional)

THE TASK

In this project, you will plan a meeting of a representative group of grade 12 students from around the province and prepare a budget proposal for travel expenses for this meeting. You will investigate a variety of options through matrix operations, spreadsheet design and use, and the fundamental counting principle.

BACKGROUND

Telephones and e-mails link people from around the world quickly and easily, but sometimes it is necessary to meet in person. Planning a meeting of many people from different locations involves the consideration of travel expenses. Organizations usually pay travel expenses for out-of-town representatives. Expenses will vary and will depend on the location of the meeting. To be as fair and cost effective as possible, meeting organizers need to consider the interplay of many factors when they choose the venue.

- Discuss some issues for which grade 12 students have valuable insight and could provide useful recommendations.
- Why is it important to have representation from different geographic regions, from urban and rural areas, and from large and small communities when important issues are discussed?
- Suggest an issue where people from different geographic areas of the province might have differing opinions.
- What are some legitimate travel expenses?
- What are the current rates for these expenses in your area?

SOURCE LINK

- To review matrices, refer to the Source Book, Chapter 2: Matrices. To review the fundamental counting principle, refer to Chapter 1: Probability.

For help with matrix operations on the TI-83 graphing calculator, see Utility 26.

The Client Service Plan
Client Service Interviews
Partnering

ORGANIZING a Meeting

GETTING STARTED

Set up a committee composed of 10 to 12 representatives according to the following guidelines.

- At least 3 from rural communities
- At least 3 from mid-size communities
- At least 3 from the largest cities
- No 2 from the same community
- At least 6 geographic areas or regions of the province represented

1. Choose an issue that involves a wide range of opinions and where input from high school students would be of interest.
2. Divide the province into 6 regions. Estimate how many rural and mid-size communities are in each region. Where are the largest three cities located?
3. Structure your committee based on your estimates of the number of communities in each region. For example, you could choose 6 rural, 3 mid-size community, and 3 city representatives; or alternatively, 3 rural, 3 mid-size community, and 4 city representatives.
4. Consider your estimates of the number of communities of each size in the province, and the number of representatives you will invite from rural, mid-size, and large-size communities. How many possible ways are there to choose representative communities?
5. Follow the guidelines and choose specific communities to be represented at the meeting.

6. Use a provincial road map to choose at least 4 possible locations for the meeting. These locations should provide suitable venues and enable the meeting to be cost effective.
7. Consider the following travel expenses: vehicle distance charge, public transportation (bus, train, plane, taxi), meals, and accommodation. Representatives will have different expenses, depending on the location of the meeting. Prepare a copy of Table A for each of the 4 potential locations you chose.

Table A

Travel expenses to attend a meeting at _____________.

Expense from:	Distance Charge: Distance to Meeting or Airport	Public Transportation Cost	Meals	Accomodation
Community 1				
Community 2				
Community 3				

Research travel options from each community and enter values in the columns of the table: distance (to meeting or airport), cost of public transportation to meeting site, number of meals, and number of nights' accommodation needed.

(If a representative drives the whole distance, public transportation will be 0.)

Create a matrix, matrix A, from each of these tables. Each of these matrices will have dimensions of $n \times 4$, where n is the number of communities represented at the meeting.

Table B: Rates for Expenses at the Meeting

Distance Charge Rate $/km				
Public Transportation	1	1	1	1
Meal Rate				
Accomodation Cost				

8. For each potential location, prepare a copy of Table B to represent different local rates for costs incurred while at the meeting. This will enable you to determine the effect of different rates of payment on the total budget.

a) Enter the following values in the first data column.
In Row 1, the current rate paid for driving one's own vehicle ($/km); in Row 2 a placeholder (1) for public transportation; in Row 3 a reasonable average rate for the purchase of a meal; and, in Row 4, a reasonable rate for accommodation at the meeting site.
Note: the actual cost of transportation is entered in Table A.

b) In the second column, enter a different set of values for these rates. For example, you may wish to pay a higher rate/kilometre for vehicle distance charge, and a lower rate for meals, or less for a vehicle and more for meals.

ORGANIZING a Meeting

c) Add more columns to investigate more rate options.

Create a matrix, matrix B, from each of these tables. Each matrix will have dimensions of $4 \times p$, where p is the number of rate options studied.

9. Select one of the potential locations.

a) Enter the data for matrix A for this location on a calculator that can perform matrix operations. What are the dimensions of this matrix? What does the number of rows represent? What does the number of columns represent?

b) Enter the data from matrix B in another matrix on the calculator. What are the dimensions of this matrix? What does the number of rows represent? What does the number of columns represent?

10. On the calculator, multiply matrix A by matrix B: $[A] \times [B]$. What are the dimensions of the product matrix? What do the values in each row and column represent?

11. On the TI-83 calculator, press [MATRX] [►] **0** to select **cumSum(** . Insert the answer from exercise 10. Press [2nd] [(–)] [)] [ENTER]. This function will give you a new matrix that provides the cumulative sum of each column of the matrix you entered. The bottom value of each column gives you the total travel budget for that particular meeting site for each set of payment rate options entered.

PROJECT PRESENTATION

Use what you learned in Getting Started to complete your project. Apply matrix multiplication and the cumulative sum to each potential meeting location. Choose the best meeting site for your committee. Use your matrix data to justify a budget proposal for the meeting. Show total costs per representative, for each expense category, and a grand total. Supply an expense claim form for the representatives.

Your project submission will contain the following components.

- A clear statement of the purpose of the meeting
- An explanation of how the community representation was allotted

- Lists of the communities represented and the potential meeting locations
- Completed data matrices for each potential meeting location
- A recommendation for the best meeting site, supported by documents
- A travel expense budget proposal (spreadsheet or matrix)
- A spreadsheet that shows a sample travel expense claim form for individuals (show the formulas used)
- A record sheet for the combined travel expense claims (show the formulas used)

Here are detailed descriptions of each person's responsibilities.

Geographer: Coordinate the gathering of information about community populations and provincial regions. Act as chief advisor in the selection of communities to be represented at the meeting.

Travel Consultant: Coordinate the gathering of travel information, including distances, available modes of transportation and costs, and available accommodation at the venue and en route from communities.

Accountant: Research travel expense guidelines and coordinate the development of financial record documents (spreadsheets). With the Geographer and the Travel Consultant, design a spreadsheet for representatives to use as an expense claim form. The expense form will need a title; a place for name, date, and home address; headings for each of the expense items; and totals. Design another spreadsheet to use as an accounting tool to organize the data from all the expense claims. This accounting record will show the names of representatives and headings for expense categories. Provide formulas for the totals of each expense category, of each representative, and a formula for the grand total. Make sure that a cross-check formula is in place to catch errors.

Group members will work together to complete all aspects of the project.

Career Opportunities

Many business executives have assistants who coordinate meetings and arrange travel schedules and locations. Service companies have been formed to organize business meetings, run conferences, and coordinate travel itineraries. Politicians usually have a staff member to help set travel agendas and arrange meetings with constituents and interest groups. Most large hotels and all convention centres employ people with experience in coordinating the various aspects of travel and related expenses.

REACTION TIME

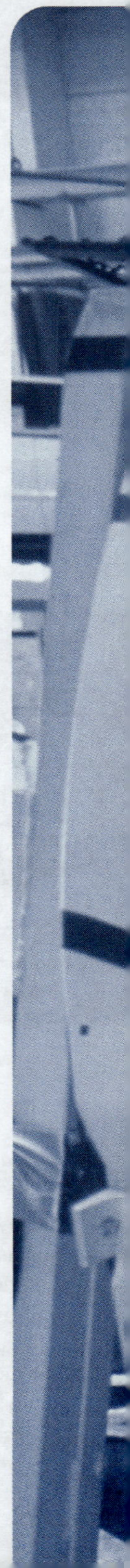

Suggested Group Size: 4

Materials: 30-cm ruler, graphing calculator

THE TASK

In this project, you will collect data concerning factors that affect human reaction time as well as investigate the effect of using a cellular phone. You will work with means, standard deviations, and *z*-scores to draw conclusions about your data.

BACKGROUND

Reaction time is a measure of how long it takes for a person to respond physically to a stimulus. When a child runs out in front of a moving car, the driver's reaction time determines how long it takes from when the driver sees the child until he or she applies the brakes. In this circumstance, the shorter the reaction time the better.

Many factors influence an individual's reaction time. When investigating an accident, investigators look for factors that might have decreased the driver's ability to respond to the event that caused the accident. Often, factors that affect reaction time may have contributed to the accident.

SOURCE LINK

- For a review of the calculation of mean, standard deviation, and z-scores, refer to the Source Book, Chapter 3: Statistics. For help with the use of the TI-83 for statistical functions, see Utilities 27 and 28.

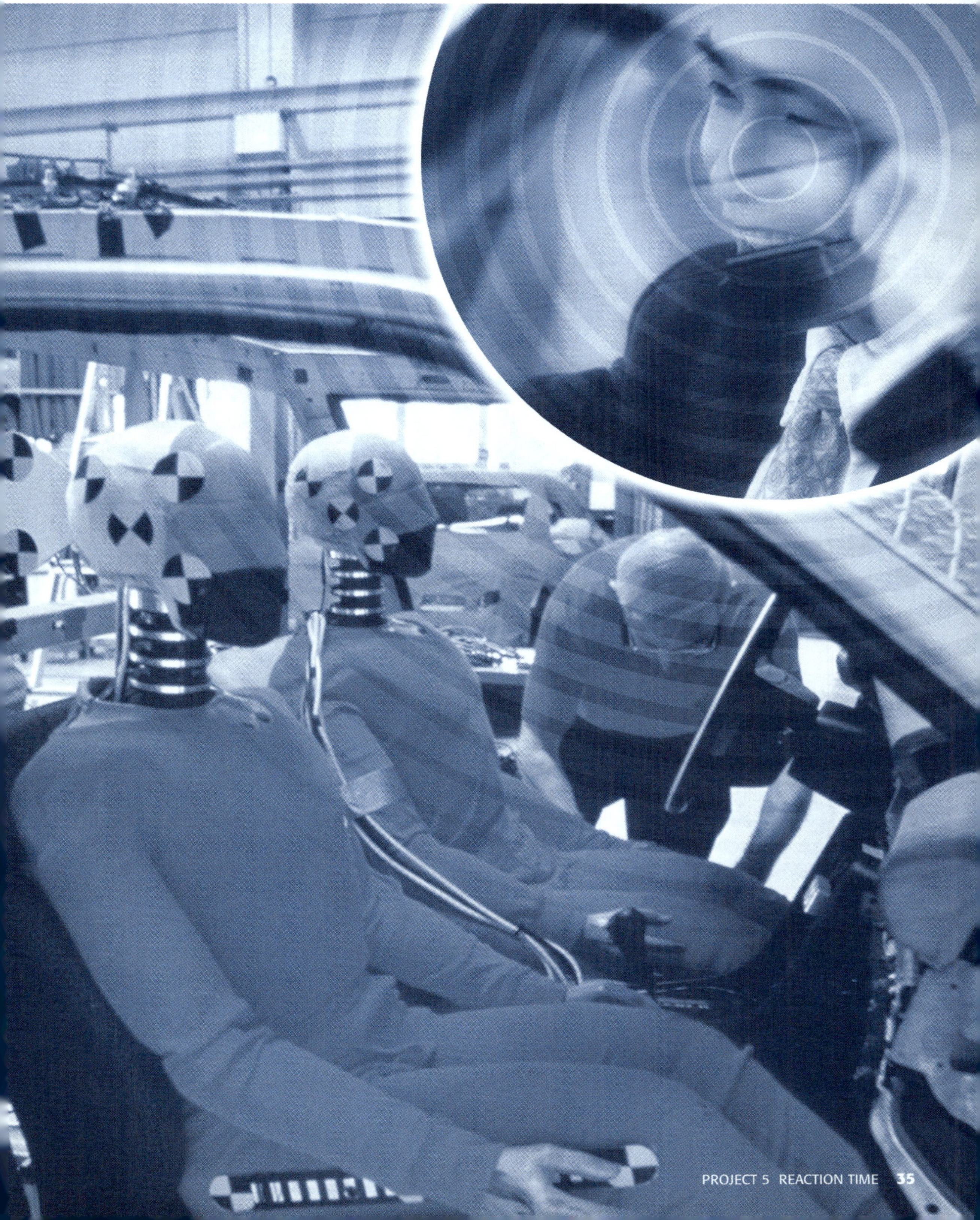

REACTION TIME

Consider the statistics in the table below. They provide information on automobile crashes that resulted in death or injury.

Year	1986	1987	1988	1989	1990
Total Number	28 948	29 737	31 462	33 551	35 660
% Driving w/o Due Care	27.8	29.0	26.5	26.0	24.9
% Alcohol Related	13.0	12.8	12.0	11.1	10.7
% Driving Unsafe Speed	15.0	15.2	16.3	16.8	15.9
% Failed to Yield	16.9	16.9	17.5	17.2	16.2
% Due to Weather	9.4	8.1	9.8	10.0	11.3
% Following Too Close	7.4	8.4	10.3	10.6	10.9
% Vehicle Fault	3.5	3.6	3.3	3.3	2.7

There may be more than one contributing factor to a crash, so the total percent may be more than 100%.

- What percent of accidents in British Columbia during 1986 were alcohol related? How has that number changed over time? What could have caused the change?
- How does alcohol consumption affect reaction time?
- How does vehicle speed affect the maximum reaction time necessary to avoid an accident?
- What might cause someone to drive without due care and attention?
- How might alcohol, speed, and other distractions affect reaction time?
- Some communities want to make it an offence to use a cellular phone while driving. Does talking on a cell phone change reaction time? To what extent could one predict the change in reaction time?
- Are there circumstances where a fast reaction time could be unsafe?

GETTING STARTED

The formula for z-score, namely

$$z = \frac{x - \mu}{\sigma}$$

expresses any value in terms of the number of standard deviations it is from the mean of the distribution.

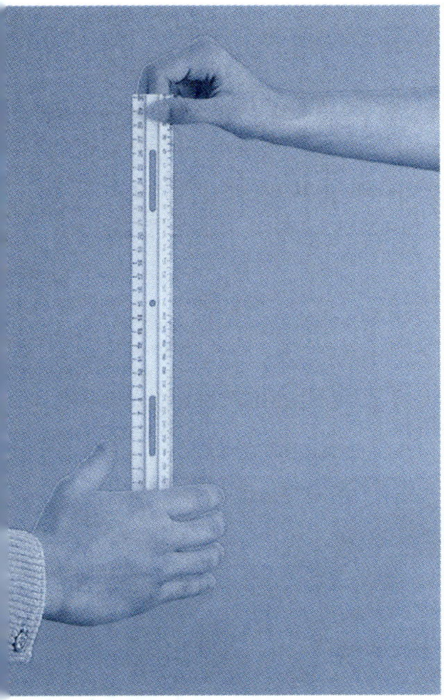

1. A survey is made of the number of hours per week that members of a class spend in sports activities or working out at the gym. The mean is 4.5 h, with a standard deviation of 0.4 h. Brian's average workout time is 4.75 h per week. What is his z-score? What does this mean about his activity level compared to those of the other students in his class? What percent of students work out fewer hours than Brian does?

2. Conduct the following activity with a partner. Have your partner suspend a 30-cm ruler as shown.

Place your fingers at the bottom of the ruler but do not allow them to touch it. Your partner will drop the ruler at a random time. Catch the ruler as quickly as you can between your thumb and forefinger. Do not move your hand downward; brace it against a table if necessary. Conduct the activity 10 times. Each time, note and record the position where the ruler was caught.

a) Use your 10 results to calculate the mean position at which you caught the ruler.

b) Determine the mean position for the whole class.

c) Determine the standard deviation for the whole class.

d) Compute your z-score based on the answers to parts a, b, and c.

e) Interpret your z-score. How does your reaction time compare to those of your classmates?

3. Create an activity to test the effect of distractions on reaction time. Examples might include talking to someone, answering math questions, listening to music, eating, or drinking. Predict how each of these might affect reaction time.

REACTION TIME

4. With your teacher's approval, perform the activity you created on a sample of students from your class. Calculate the mean and standard deviation of the reaction time under the test conditions. Analyze the results and interpret the scores.

PROJECT PRESENTATION

Research the effect of using a cellular phone on reaction time and write a report to respond to a proposed new law that bans the use of cell phones while driving. Create an activity to measure the effect that talking on a cell phone has on reaction time. Use the ruler-drop method from Getting Started to determine reaction time.

Your completed project will include the following.

- A description of the experiment, the selection of participants, and the results

- Calculations of means, standard deviations, and z-scores
- A conclusion about the relationship between talking on a cell phone and reaction time

- A statement that discusses factors, other than reaction time, that might be affected when a person talks on a cell phone. An example might be the difficulty shifting gears on a car with standard transmission while the driver holds a cell phone.

Here is a detailed explanation of each person's responsibilities.

Experimenters (2): Design an experiment to determine how reaction time is affected by talking on a cell phone. Make a random selection of subjects and perform the experiment in a standardized way. Record the data in tables.

Data Analyst (1): Analyze the data, interpret the results, and present them to your group. Compare your group's experimental data to the class data on reaction time, found in Getting Started. Suggest a conclusion based on statistics.

Reporter (1): Collect the opinions of group members regarding your experiment. Present your conclusions in a report and explain how your data and analysis support them. Incorporate other important issues concerned with cell phones in your recommendations for the proposed law.

Career Opportunities

Decisions on laws that govern individual activities, such as cell phone use, are based on experimental data, research, and opinion polls. Researchers, data analysts, and statisticians collect, collate, and interpret data. Social scientists, psychologists, lawyers, and writers are needed to implement the results and convince the public to respect the law.

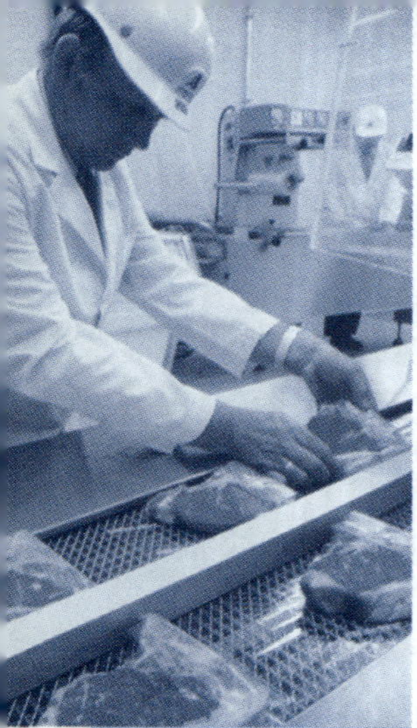

QUALITY CONTROL

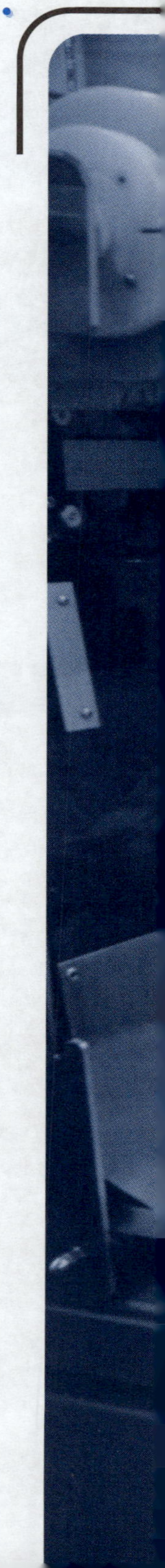

THE TASK

In this project, you will investigate quality control in industry. You will construct and interpret a control chart to decide whether to modify a manufacturing process. You will work with means, standard deviations, ranges, upper and lower control limits, and confidence intervals.

Suggested Group Size: 3

Materials: Graphing calculator, grid paper, a Vernier caliper or a top-loading balance, 200 jelly beans or 200 galvanized nails; a computer with statistical and graphing software (optional)

SOURCE LINK

- If you wish to review means, standard deviation, and confidence intervals, refer to the Source Book, Chapter 3: Statistics. For help with the use of the TI-83 for statistical functions, see Utilities 27 and 28.

BACKGROUND

Quality control is critical in a wide variety of industries. Most producers attempt to make the dimensions of their product conform to certain limits. In many cases these limits are required for safety reasons. One of the basic tools of statistical process control is the control chart, in which the value of some aspect of the product is tracked over time.

For example, a meat packer might want the average fat content of ground beef to be 25%. It is not possible to have exactly 25% fat in every package of ground beef, so the packer sets maximum and minimum allowable limits on fat content. The beef packer collects random samples of ground beef and measures the fat content. The mean and range of the values are recorded and tracked over time using $\bar{x}$ and R control charts. The $\bar{x}$-chart shows the means of random samples of the product taken over some time period. The R-chart refers to the ranges of the samples. The control chart shows the 2 measures concurrently. The measured fat content should fall well within the specified limits, with the number of samples containing more than 25% fat being roughly the same as those with less than 25%.

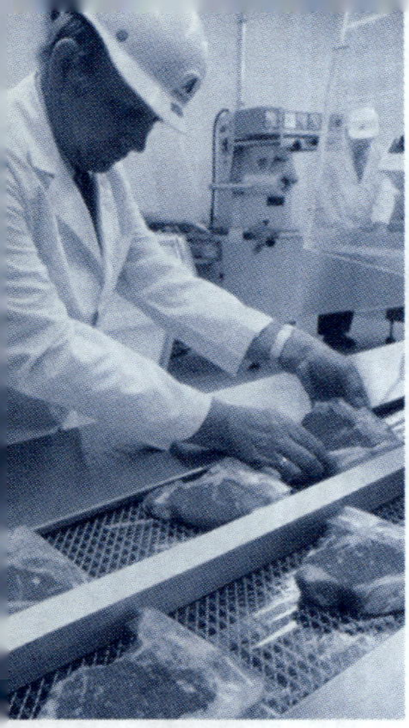

QUALITY CONTROL

- Why is product uniformity often important?
- List some industries where non-uniform products could result in safety problems.
- Are there any products where non-uniformity is an asset?
- How might you set limits on a range of measurements? Apply the idea of standard deviation to this problem.

GETTING STARTED

1. The heights of Canadian women approximate a normal distribution, with a mean of 162.6 cm and a standard deviation of 6.4 cm. What percent of the female population do you expect to have heights between 154 cm and 172 cm?

2. The masses of apples in a shipment are normally distributed, with a mean of 110 g and a standard deviation of 16 g. Without using your calculator, state a range of masses that includes 68% of the apples.

3. A meat packing plant operates 24 h per day. Over a period of 8 d, 5 random samples of ground beef are chosen per 8-h shift. The fat content of each sample is measured and the average fat content, $\bar{x}$, and the range of fat content, R, of the 5 samples are recorded. The data are shown to the right. Construct an $\bar{x}$ and R control chart for these data.

Fat Content (% by weight)

Shift	$\bar{x}$	R	Shift	$\bar{x}$	R
1	24.7	2.3	13	25.1	3.8
2	25.5	4.1	14	24.6	3.3
3	25.0	5.2	15	24.2	3.6
4	25.2	3.1	16	25.8	4.5
5	26.3	1.7	17	25.5	3.8
6	28.4	3.5	18	24.0	4.1
7	26.2	2.2	19	24.3	2.9
8	24.7	4.1	20	26.1	4.2
9	24.5	3.7	21	23.8	3.0
10	24.6	6.3	22	25.4	5.3
11	23.4	1.4	23	26.0	5.2
12	22.9	2.5	24	25.3	5.0

a) Enter the shift number in L1, the means of the samples, $\bar{x}$, in L2, and the ranges of the samples, R, in L3 on your TI-83 calculator, or computer.

b) Calculate the mean and standard deviation of the means of the samples. This mean of means, the grand average, determines the centre line, CL, on the control chart. The upper control limit, (UCL), is at 3 standard deviations above the grand average. The lower control limit, (LCL), is at 3 standard deviations below the grand average. Determine the values of UCL and LCL for these data.

c) With shift number on the x-axis and % fat content on the y-axis, plot the control chart lines, CL, UCL, and LCL. Use grid paper or the TI-83 calculator. If you are using the TI-83, choose an appropriate window. In the Y= list set the value for CL as Y1; the value for UCL as Y2; and the value for LCL as Y3.

d) Plot the STAT PLOT of the data for the means of the samples on the control chart. Use the first two TI–83 screens shown below to create the graph. Your completed $\bar{x}$ graph on the TI-83 should look like the third screen below.

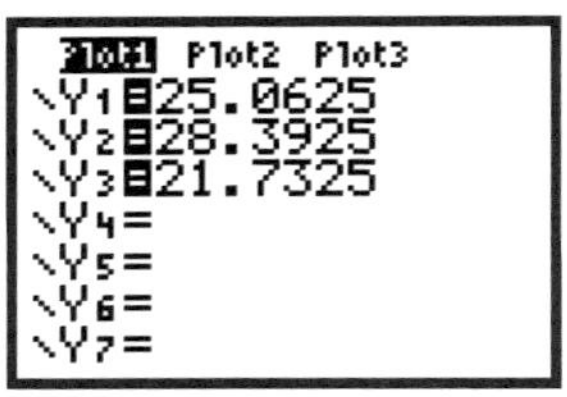

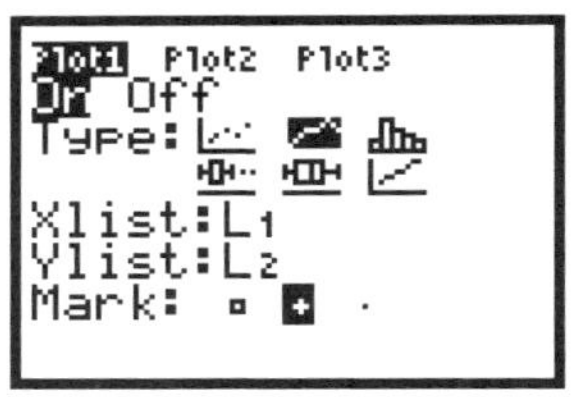

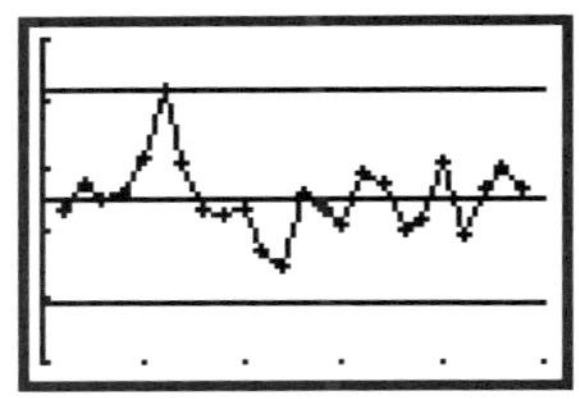

If we express these values as z-scores, the control chart will have its centre line at $z = 0$ and its upper and lower control limits at $z = 3$ and $z = -3$, respectively. All the points fall within the control limits, although one point is slightly above the UCL.
If a point were to fall above the UCL, it would be reasonable to conclude that something occurred during that shift to cause the fat content to be too high. Quality will benefit if management and staff can pinpoint the cause and correct it.

e) Repeat parts b and c to generate the R-chart and complete the $\bar{x}$ and R control charts.

4. The UCL and the LCL are at 3 standard deviations from the mean.

a) How much of the distribution is included within them?

b) What is the probability that a point will fall outside these limits by chance alone?

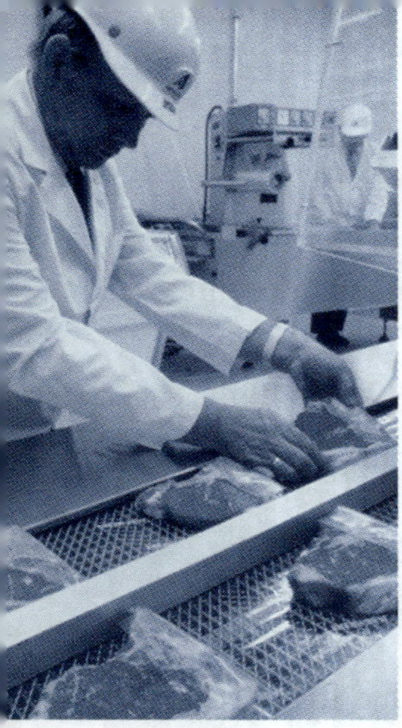

QUALITY CONTROL

Interpreting Control Charts

Patterns or trends within control charts may indicate that problems are developing within the manufacturing process. Some rules of thumb are:

- Points that fall outside the control limits can be attributed to "assignable cause," which can be corrected by modifying production.
- Seven or more points in a row either above or below the centre line indicate that some aspect of the production process is off target.
- Seven or more points in a row either increasing or decreasing indicate a change in the production process.
- Points should not follow a repeating cycle.

When all points fall within the specified limits and none of the trends described above are present, the process is said to be within statistical control.

5. Is the fat content of the ground beef within statistical control?

In real life, $\overline{x}$ and R charts have to be modified slightly because of the nature of data collection.

PROJECT PRESENTATION

A. Analyze Data from Production

A metal plate with a hole in it is being manufactured. The diameter of the hole is to be 255.00 mm. During each production shift, 5 plates are randomly selected and measured. For the data in the table, generate an $\overline{x}$ and R control chart. Explain whether the manufacturing process is in statistical control or whether it should be modified. Comment on any trends in the data.

Hole Diameter (mm)

Shift	$\overline{x}$	R	Shift	$\overline{x}$	R
1	255.40	0.42	11	254.95	0.47
2	254.99	0.46	12	254.98	0.45
3	255.22	0.39	13	255.07	0.43
4	255.39	0.41	14	255.12	0.50
5	254.95	0.48	15	255.08	0.45
6	255.21	0.36	16	255.27	0.45
7	254.98	0.45	17	255.31	0.44
8	255.31	0.43	18	255.26	0.46
9	255.48	0.44	19	255.21	0.49
10	255.06	0.48	20	255.29	0.45

B. Simulate a Sampling Process

Choose the method of simulation suitable for the equipment available in your class.

a) Measure the length of individual jelly beans or galvanized nails with a Vernier caliper.

b) Determine the mass of individual jelly beans or galvanized nails on a top-loading balance.

i) Select five items at random and measure them or determine their masses.

ii) Record the mean and range of the sample items.

iii) Repeat the sampling 25 times and determine the grand average and standard deviation for the means and ranges.

iv) Set up a control chart and plot the data.

v) State conclusions about the manufacturing process.

Your completed project will consist of the following.

- Complete $\bar{x}$ and R charts for the metal plate scenario in part B
- Complete $\bar{x}$ and R charts for the simulation experiment in part A
- A written report that describes your interpretations for each situation

Here are detailed descriptions of each person's responsibilities.

Statisticians (2): Analyze the data and generate $\bar{x}$ and R control charts for the metal plate scenario and for the simulation. Determine whether each situation is in statistical control.

Process Engineer (1): Prepare the group's report on the metal plate and simulation control charts and interpretations of the processes. Explain why 3 standard deviations above and below the grand average are used as control limits. Relate these limits to confidence intervals.

Career Opportunities

People who are skilled in the use and interpretation of statistics find employment opportunities in quality control in industry. Those who can interpret and communicate statistical results are needed in marketing and public relations.

Un-Designer Jeans

Suggested Group Size: 3

Materials: A graphing calculator, grid paper, and construction paper; a computer with a spreadsheet program (optional)

THE TASK

In this project, you will design an "individual brand" pair of unisex jeans for the young adult market and investigate some aspects of garment production. You will work with design, layout, costing, and statistics, including standard deviation, z-scores, confidence intervals, and creating sample spaces.

BACKGROUND

For many young people, the Nike swoosh and Tommy or CK logos have become symbols of marketing's manipulation of society's so-called needs. Branding of all kinds of goods and services has become a multi-billion dollar industry in North America. Having the right brand patch on jeans has been all-important and patches are a hot counterfeit item in some areas of the world. However, teens always want to express their individuality. Many are now opting out of the various brand-name fads in clothing and want to individualize their wardrobes.

Jeans are still a staple in the clothing industry, but there are many possible design options to allow for personal preferences.

- If you were to buy a new pair of jeans today, would you look for a particular brand or style?
- Do you know what size you would get?
- Where is the brand label displayed on most jeans?
- Do you think your friends would look for the same brand or style?

SOURCE LINK

- For a review of sample spaces, refer to the Source Book, Chapter 1: Probability. For distributions and z-scores, see Chapter 3: Statistics. For help with the use of the TI-83 for statistical functions, see Utilities 27 and 28.

Un-Designer Jeans

- What varieties of styles are available in jeans in the retail market?
- How might you customize a design for jeans and still be able to follow a production process?

GETTING STARTED

You may wish to use a spreadsheet for exercises 3 and 4.

1. Up-To-Date Jeans Co. plans to offer different options:
- straight or flared leg
- zipper or button fly
- contrast stitching or no contrast
- zipper or loop and button closure for back pocket

To have all these options available, how many styles must the company offer in each size?

2. Logo-Patch Jeans has a distinctive stamp set for its brand logo. The stamp set is composed of 3 patches: 1 hexagon, 1 pentagon, and 1 square. Each is designed so that rotation of the patch changes the look of the patch. How many possible stamp sets are available for Logo-Patch to advertise?

3. Denim cloth is made in rolls or bolts of a fixed width. Suppose denim retails at \$7.99/m. A wholesaler offers an 80-m bolt for \$400, with a discount of 15% on an order of more than 5 bolts. Medium-size jeans require 2.5 m and excess material can be sold for \$3.00/m.

a) What is the cost per pair of jeans under each condition of purchase?

b) Michel wishes to make a small number of custom-designed jeans. At what number of pairs of jeans does the 80-m bolt become a more economical purchase than buying the denim at a retail store?

4. An estimate was made of some of the variables involved in the production of jeans:
Denim Cloth: 2.5 m (at any of the prices in exercise 3).
Miscellaneous Items (thread, fasteners, cloth for pocket linings): \$1.15 per pair

Labour:	Cutting—0.25 h @ \$18.00/h
	Stitching—1.25 h @ \$8.15/h
	Finishing—0.5 h @ \$6.85/h

Estimate the cost to the producer for the materials and labour to manufacture a pair of jeans under each condition of denim purchase.

5. For adult females waist size is normally distributed, with a mean of 29.5 inches and a standard deviation of 2.1 inches. Assume adult jeans come in size increments of 1 inch, beginning at 24 inches. What waist sizes will a company have to provide if it wishes to cover at least 90% of the market?

6. As a class, survey your school to determine the sizes by waist and inseam (leg) measurements (in inches) of jeans bought. Decide on an appropriate sample size and prepare a survey form. Set up a size grid, with waist sizes along the vertical axis and leg lengths along the horizontal axis. Record numbers in the grid for each size. Based on your survey size, what margin of error might you expect in your results? For display purposes, make a three-dimensional histogram by stacking cardboard cutouts on a large version of the grid. This will be the master size grid for the survey data.

Un-Designer Jeans

PROJECT PRESENTATION

Use what you learned in Getting Started to begin your project. Investigate the possibility of producing a line of "one-of-a-kind" jeans. Consider waist sizes and leg lengths. Target your production to approximately the middle 95% of the population.

Your completed project will include the following.

- A scale pattern of a pair of jeans, including the extra cloth needed for sewing seams and finishing at the belt-line and cuffs
- A diagram to show how you would lay out your design pattern on the cloth
- A diagram to show how the layout would change from the smallest to the largest sizes of jeans
- An estimate of the cost of cloth purchased in your area, for various sizes of jeans
- An estimate of the labour cost per pair of jeans
- A plan for a stamp-set logo to make each pair of jeans unique (up to a maximum of 10 000 different possible arrangements of the stamp set)
- A market analysis to show what sizes to make and in what quantities

Here is a description of each person's responsibilities.

Designer: Create the design for your jeans with style options. Make a scale diagram to show the amount of denim needed. Draw the layout of the pattern on the cloth for various sizes of jeans. Develop suitable patch stamp faces to maximize the number of individual patches. A possible method for the patches is shown below.

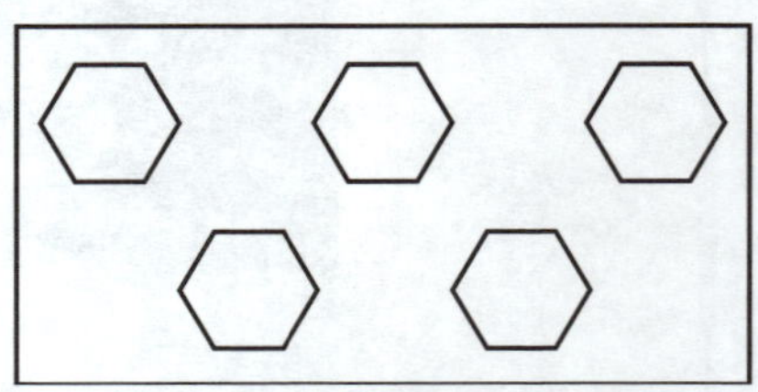

A design of 5 simple stamp faces is to be stamped onto a blank jean patch of suitable size. From 1 to 5 stamps will be put in a die (example shown to the right) and pressed with a lever to emboss the label onto the patch at the time the jeans are purchased. Stamps may be rotated in the hexagonal holes and placed in any of the locations, but may not overlap. How many distinct patch labels could be made from this stamp set? What is the probability of 2 patches being exactly the same?

Market Analyst: Prepare the data sheets and keep records of size data. Co-ordinate the work of the group with the class to obtain size data and prepare the master size grid. Choose the most popular waist size from the master size grid for further analysis. Use the frequency data on leg length for this waist size and plot a histogram. Determine the mean and standard deviation of these data. Determine the z-score for each leg length in your chosen size. Repeat these calculations for the next 2 larger and smaller waist sizes. From the z-score data, predict the percent of total purchases in each size and leg length. Prepare a market analysis and a production order for 50 000 pairs of jeans in 5 waist sizes and a variety of leg lengths.

Production/Sales Advisor: Co-ordinate the pattern layout and provide advice on patch stamp face suitability. Research the cost of denim cloth and the required miscellaneous items in your area and present an estimate of the cost of materials and the cost of labour per pair of jeans.

Career Opportunities

The research and development of any product, process, or service involve many skills of design, layout, costing, and analysis. The retail industry depends on the skills of many people to get products from the drawing board to the consumer. Specific career areas that require these skills are marketing, advertisement, design, inventory control, and management.

TO LEA$E OR PURCHA$E?

THE TASK

In this project, you will examine costs involved in providing sports equipment at a recreational resort. You will research the cost and approximate rate of depreciation of equipment, and compare the options of lease or purchase to select the optimum for your business.

Suggested Group Size: 2

Materials: Computer with spreadsheet program, graphing calculator, newspaper classified ads, or other classifieds; Internet access (optional)

SOURCE LINK

- For a comparison of leasing and purchasing, refer to the Source Book, Chapter 4: Personal Finance.

If you need help to format spreadsheets, see Utility 31; for the use of the TVM Solver, refer to Utility 22 in *Applied Mathematics 11* or available from your teacher.

BACKGROUND

Have you been to a recreational resort and wondered why all the equipment looks new? The answer is that much of it is leased. Resort owners know that, to attract clients, they must have up-to-date facilities. Leasing also eliminates any problems associated with resale or trade-in.

There are other advantages to leasing as well.

- Customized payment schedules suit particular needs; you may choose a term and lease to meet budget requirements.
- Money is saved on income tax; lease payments can be 100% tax deductible as an operating expense, whereas only a portion of capital purchases are deductible each year.
- Capital is conserved, not tied up in equipment purchases; money is available for unexpected expenses.

When you lease an item, you rent it from the owner. Your monthly payments cover the depreciation of the item over the term of the lease plus interest on the outstanding balance of the full price of the item. Since you do not purchase the item, you pay taxes only on the monthly lease amount, rather than on the complete purchase price.

TO LEA$E OR PURCHA$E?

Imagine that you purchase a year-round recreational resort located on a large lake. You wish to set up sporting facilities and equipment to attract a young, fitness-conscious clientele.

- List the sports that you might find at such a resort.
- List the equipment required for these sports. What equipment must the resort have available? What equipment will each guest bring?
- Some equipment, such as golf carts and clubs, will be available for rent; other equipment, such as volleyball nets, will be provided free of charge. Items, such as lawnmowers, are considered to be maintenance equipment. They are regarded as a capital cost to buy, but an operating cost to run and repair.
- How will you, the resort owner, finance this equipment? Is it necessary to own all of the equipment, or is it important merely to have the use of it?
- What are factors to consider when you decide whether to lease or purchase various types of equipment?

GETTING STARTED

There is no one correct answer to the question of whether to lease or purchase equipment. Some factors to consider are:

- Cash on hand; whether a loan is needed to purchase the equipment
- Length of time before the equipment is replaced
- Residual value of the equipment
- The demand for used equipment — if the resort were to try to sell the equipment privately, would it sell easily?

Complete the exercises to gain an understanding of lease and purchase agreements.

1. The purchase price of a hydraulic mower, with a life expectancy of 4 years, is $31 500. A golf course requires 6 such mowers to keep the greens well manicured. The choice is between lease and purchase.

a) What is the purchase price of the 6 mowers?

b) What is the total cost, including taxes, to purchase the mowers? (Assume PST is 7%.)

c) Use your TVM Solver to determine the monthly payment if the mowers are financed for

i) 4 years at 8.5%, compounded monthly.

ii) 3 years at the same interest rate.

iii) 2 years at the same interest rate.

d) Suppose the purchase is financed over 4 years at 8.5%, compounded monthly.

i) How much would be owing after 3 years?

ii) How much would be owing after 2 years?

iii) The residual value of the mowers at the end of 3 years is 30% of the purchase price. If the resort owners were to sell the mowers at this point, would they receive money or would they still owe money?

iv) The residual value at the end of 2 years is 52% of the purchase price. If the resort owners were to sell the mowers at this point, how much money would they still owe?

TO LEA$E OR PURCHA$E?

e) The resort operator has the option to lease the mowers for a 3-year term at 9%, compounded monthly.

i) What is the monthly lease payment before taxes? Use your TVM Solver to determine the payments. (The present value is the price before taxes. The future value is the residual value. The interest on the outstanding balance is automatically included in the calculation.)

ii) What is the payment including taxes?

f) Alternatively, the mowers could be leased for 2 years at 9%, compounded monthly. What is the monthly lease payment, including taxes, for this term?

g) Examine your results for parts c to f. Why might a lease be the better alternative for the resort?

h) List any advantages there may be to a purchase.

2. If the resort operator is able to pay cash for the mowers, is there any advantage to a lease?

3. Another option is to lease the mowers at the beginning of the golf season, and to make payments during May to October only.

a) Why might the resort operator want to make this arrangement?

b) Do you think the payments would be higher, lower, or the same? Explain.

4. A set of cross-country skis can be purchased for $349, plus taxes.

a) The leasing company is willing to lease 10 pairs of skis, financed at 12% interest, compounded monthly, for 2 years, with a monthly payment of $144.88, plus taxes. What is the residual value of the skis, expressed as a percent of the purchase price?

b) A second option is to lease the skis for 1 year at the same interest rate. The monthly payment would be $213.77. What is the residual value at the end of 1 year?

c) What would the monthly payment be if the skis were purchased, then financed at 11% interest, compounded monthly, over 24 months? over 12 months? (Assume 7% PST.)

d) Under these circumstances, would you purchase the skis or lease them? Explain.

PROJECT PRESENTATION

Use what you learned in Getting Started to begin your project. You will plan the activities to be offered, the equipment needed, and the method of financing for different types of equipment. You will keep the operation of the sports activities separate from the other expenses of the resort.

Your completed project will include the following:

- A brief description of the activities to be offered
- A list of the equipment needed and its seasonal usage
- A discussion of costs, and rates of depreciation and replacement of equipment
- A comparison of financing needed for the purchase or lease of equipment
- A table of costs of purchase or lease of specific items
- A budget for each season

Here is a detailed description of each person's responsibilities.

Program Director: Determine what activities will be offered within a year-round or seasonal operation. Make a list of the number and price of each type of equipment required. Categorize each item as major or minor equipment. (For example: a Sea-Doo is major equipment; sets of horseshoes are minor equipment.) Make decisions about how frequently you will replace equipment, and estimate its resale, or residual, value at that point. Decide what clothing and footwear you will rent and what sizes you will stock.

TO LEA$E OR PURCHA$E?

Research resort and equipment suppliers on the Internet to cost your equipment list or use typical costs supplied in Table 1. Determine resale values from classified advertisements, or make estimates using the rule of thumb shown in Table 2.

Present your results in tables.

Work with the business manager to make a table of the seasonal usage of the equipment.

Table 1 Cost Chart for Sports Equipment

Summer				Winter	
Water Sports	**Cost**	**Land Sports**	**Cost**		**Cost**
Canoe	$1275	Badminton gear	$26	Snowmobile	$7 990
Fishing boat	$1459	Volleyball gear	$555	Clothing, helmet	$350
Outboard motor	$2380	In-line skates	$135	X-country skis	$349
Pedal boat	$519	Pads and helmet	$70	Snowmobile boots	$150
Sailboat	$1039	Set of horseshoes	$40	Portable ice fishing house	$415
Rowboat	$829	Mountain bike	$249	Snowplow	$4 465
Sailboard	$675			Toboggan	$40
Sea-Doo	$8179	**Golf Course**	**Cost**	**Year-Round Health Spa**	**Cost**
Fishing rod & reel	$129	Hydraulic mowers	$31 500	Multi-station gym	$10 399
Life jacket	$43	Rental clubs	$250	Treadmill	$1 200
		Electric cart	$2 969	Stairclimber	$1 925
		Pull cart	$185	Exercise bike	$349

Table 2

Item	Annual Depreciation Rate (percent of previous year's value)
Motorized equipment	30% to 35%
Other major equipment	20%
Minor equipment	40%

Business Manager: Research current interest rates for business loans. Decide the terms of the loan for each major piece of equipment, and a term for a loan for the minor piece of equipment. Calculate the monthly payment required to pay off the loans.

If possible, research interest rates on leases of the various equipment, or obtain actual leasing information. Determine the monthly lease payment required for each item and whether payments should be made year-round or seasonal. Set up a table of the cost to lease and to purchase each item. Include columns with your recommendation on whether to lease or purchase, and on the form any lease should take. Explain your reasoning. Prepare a budget for each season and state the monthly revenue required to meet the loan and lease obligations.

Career Opportunities

Leasing is increasing in popularity each year. There are opportunities for entrepreneurs to start their own leasing companies. The popularity of resorts is increasing, with opportunities for directors and managers. These people need to be able to forecast future needs of clientele, to make decisions regarding equipment, and to set and follow careful budgets to ensure that a resort is profitable, yet affordable for the public.

INVESTING IN THE Stock MarkeT

PLAYING WITH BULLS AND BEARS!

Suggested Group Size: 2

Materials: Newspapers that contain weekly stock market listings; computer with spreadsheet program, Internet access (optional)

SOURCE LINK

- For an explanation of investment portfolios and investment types, refer to the Source Book, Chapter 4: Personal Finance, *Tutorial 4.3:* Investment Portfolios.

If you need help to format spreadsheets, see Utility 31.

THE TASK

In this project, you will examine the stock market. One member of your group will track individual stocks, while the other will track mutual funds. You will select, track, and record the weekly closing prices of your stocks or mutual funds for 13 or 26 weeks. At the end of the project, you will determine your capital gain (or loss!).

BACKGROUND

Stocks and mutual funds are equity investments. They offer a greater potential return on your money than cash or fixed income investments, but involve greater risk. They should be considered to be long-term investments, because it may take several years to realize high returns. Equity investments are classified as "growth" investments. When you invest in the stock market, you become a partial owner of the company whose stock you purchase, and may be paid a portion of the company's earnings in the form of dividends. You also hope to realize capital appreciation, or capital gains, when you sell your stock for a profit. However not all stocks appreciate over time. Returns can vary widely from year to year and different equities have different risk levels. You may actually lose money, which is termed a capital loss.

Stock markets can fluctuate very quickly. As an investor, you must not panic when the market takes a sudden dip, as in the sudden crash of technology stocks in April 2000.

Many Canadians who cannot afford to purchase several different stocks, or do not have the time to track the stock market, may put their money in mutual funds.

The Alberta Stock Exchange

INVESTING IN THE Stock Market

PLAYING WITH BULLS AND BEARS!

With a mutual fund, your money is pooled with the money of many other investors. A professional fund manager invests in a variety of securities, depending on the fund's specific objectives. Funds may contain only Canadian stocks, or could include stocks from Europe, the Far East, or the Americas. Some fund categories are growth funds, emerging market funds, balanced funds, and bond funds.

Investing in the stock market is easier when you know the terms.

In a bear market, securities prices are generally falling. In a bull market, prices rise over a prolonged period. According to legend, these terms are used because a bear lowers his head when he charges while a bull tosses his horns up!

You can use an index to measure the performance of a market. For example, the TSE (Toronto Stock Exchange) 300 Composite Index averages the performance of the stocks of 300 of the largest Canadian companies. You may have heard on the business news "the Index closed up 30 points today." This indicates that on that particular day, most stocks rose in price, or, the positive influence of those that rose offset any negative influences from those that fell.

A board lot is a unit of trading. When you buy or sell stocks, you generally do so in board lots. Board lots on the TSE are:

- Shares under $0.10: 1000 shares
- Shares between $0.10 and $0.99: 500 shares
- Shares $1 or more: 100 shares

Refer to financial brochures, or search the Internet, for other investment terms.

- Your list should include bid and ask, common shares, futures, preferred shares, price/earnings ratio.
- What are the advantages and disadvantages of investing in mutual funds?
- What fees are involved when an investor buys or sells stocks or mutual funds?

GETTING STARTED

1. Imagine that you have $10 000 to invest. The first step is to choose stocks. You could invest in just one stock but a better strategy is to diversify. Pick a large number of stocks and invest small amounts in each one. Begin your selection by considering stocks from several different categories. These categories include:

Mines and Minerals	Oil and Gas	Communications and Media
Integrated Mines Mining Gold and Precious Metals	Integrated Oils Oil and Gas Producers Oil and Gas Services	Broadcasting Cable and Entertainment Publishing and Printing
Consumer Products	**Industrial Products**	**Merchandising**
Food Processing Tobacco Breweries and Beverages Household Goods Biotechnology/Pharmaceuticals	Steels Fabricating and Engineering Transportation Equipment Technology — hardware Technology — software Building Materials Chemicals and Fertilizers Automobiles and Parts	Wholesale Distributions Food Stores Department Stores Specialty Stores Hospitality Online Services
Utilities	**Transportation/Environmental Services**	**Financial Services**
Telephone Gas/Electrical	Leisure Transportation Transportation Companies Waste Management Companies	Banks and Trusts Investment Companies Insurance Financial Management Companies
Real Estate	**Paper and Forest Products**	**Pipelines**
Income Property Companies Hotels	Lumber Companies Paper Manufacturers Income Trusts	Oil Pipelines Gas Pipelines

2. For this project, you will buy one board lot of each stock. Choose 10 or more different stocks so that the total purchase price is approximately $10 000. You may wish to examine the listed companies on the Internet to obtain the complete company name and its symbol. Select Canadian sites on your browser, and then locate stock exchanges in the finance section.

3. If you are investing in mutual funds, choose 10 different funds and invest \$1000 in each fund. You could select several funds from 1 company, or 10 different companies. Browse the finance section of the Internet to learn more about these funds. The Internet will contain graphs and charts that indicate the fund's performance for the past few years. Use this information to assist you in making your choices.

4. Enter your stocks or mutual funds on a spreadsheet, as shown, then sort them alphabetically. If you purchase stocks, enter the number of shares purchased, and then calculate the purchase price for each stock. Obtain these prices from the weekly closing price in your newspaper. For the mutual funds, each purchase price will be \$1000. Calculate the total purchase price for the entire portfolio.

	A	B	C	D
1				*- Date -*
2				Week 1
3	Name of Stock or Fund	Number of Shares Purchased	Price per Share	Purchase Price
4				
5				
6				
	TOTALS			\$ xxxxx.xx

5. Create a graph to track your portfolio for each week of the project. Plot the purchase price of your portfolio as the point for Week 1.

PROJECT PRESENTATION

Use what you learned in Getting Started and continue your project for 13 or 26 weeks.

1. Each week, check the newspaper to find the closing weekly price for your chosen stocks or funds and the change in price. Enter these values onto your spreadsheet.
   IF YOU DO NOT FIND A STOCK, it means that no trading was done in that particular stock that week and the price is the same as the previous week. Enter the previous week's close. The change will be 0.
   CAUTION: Many companies have stocks with the same name, but different symbols. Check the stock whose name and symbols match your stock EXACTLY.

2. Find the total each week. The closing price for the current week minus the change in price should be equal to the closing price for the previous week for each stock. This should also be true for the totals. Check your numbers for accuracy.

   For example:
   - Stock ABC has a closing price of \$8.50 and a change of \$0.25. This means that last week's closing price was \$8.50 – \$0.25, or \$8.25.
   - Stock XYZ has a closing price of \$11.75 and a change of –\$1.50. This means that last week's closing price was \$11.75 – \$(–1.50) = \$13.25.

	A	B	C	D	E	F	G	H
1				*– Date –*	*– Date –*		*– Date*	
2				Week 1	Week 2		Week 3	
3	Name of Stock or Fund	Number of Shares Purchased	Price per Share	Purchase Price	Close	Change	Close	Change
4								
5								
6								
	TOTALS							

3. Observe and record the total value of your investment each week. Update your graph.

INVESTING IN THE

Stock Market

PLAYING WITH BULLS AND BEARS!

4. At the end of the project (after either 13 or 26 weeks), calculate the summary column as follows:

Capital gain (or loss) = Last price – Initial price
(This is the profit or loss for either 13 or 26 weeks.)

$$\text{Percent gain (or loss)} = \frac{\text{Capital gain (or loss)}}{\text{Initial purchase price}} \times 100$$

(This is the percent profit or loss for 13 or 26 weeks.)

Calculate your *total* profit (or loss).

Calculate your *total* percent profit (or loss).

	A	B	C	D	E					
1				- Date -	- Date -		- Date			
2				Week 1	Week 2		Final Week			
3	Name of Stock or Fund	Number of Shares Purchased	Price per Share	Purchase Price	Close	Change	Close	Change	Capital Gain (or Loss)	% Gain (or Loss)
4										
5										
6										
9	**TOTALS**									

5. The profit was calculated for either 13 or 26 weeks. If the rate of growth in the value of your stocks were maintained, your annual profit (or loss) would be 4 times or 2 times this amount. What would it be? Compare this to the amount you would earn if you kept your money in a savings account or in bonds.

Your final project will consist of the following:

- A printout of your spreadsheets
- The graphs of the value of your stocks and mutual funds
- A written comment on each individual stock or fund. Why do you think it rose or fell? Was it a good investment? Would you keep it or sell it?
- A comparison of the earnings of the stock portfolio and the mutual fund portfolio

Here is a detailed description of each person's responsibilities.

Investment Analysts (2): Work together to set up and follow the performance of a stock portfolio and a mutual fund portfolio. Enter your stocks or funds on spreadsheets, create graphs to track their performance, and calculate capital gains or losses. Compare the earnings of stocks and mutual funds, and prepare a discussion of the advantages and disadvantages of investing in individual stocks versus mutual funds.

Career Opportunities

A financial advisor provides effective, knowledgeable advice to clients on a wide range of investment opportunities. He or she is able to plan and anticipate a client's short- and long-term needs. An advisor must pass the Canadian Securities Course. Advisors are paid commissions on all transactions. Commissions range from $30 000 to $1.2 million per year, based on performance.

Landscape *Gardening*

Suggested Group Size: 2

Materials: Graphing calculator, grid paper, a computer with a spreadsheet program

THE TASK

In this project, you will design and calculate costs for a garden suitable for a condominium complex, apartment building, or university residence. You will measure dimensions, perimeters, areas, and volumes, and use estimation, unit pricing, layouts, and templates for financial spreadsheets.

BACKGROUND

Many condominium complexes, apartment buildings, and university residences have gardens that provide an attractive green space for residents. The garden area may contain a lawn, small trees, flowers, shrubs, benches, and even a pond or fountain.

Architects work closely with landscape artists to integrate the designs for buildings and gardens. A landscape artist is responsible for a project from the design stage to completion. Landscape artists need to know what flowers bloom in the various seasons, which plants must be replaced each year, and which will bloom for several years. They must know how to plant a lawn and construct a pond or fountain. They must be able to estimate the total costs of the project, including those for creative design, labour, plants, and materials such as topsoil, rocks, and paving stones. They must track their costs and present an invoice to the developer when the garden is finished.

- What species of ornamental trees may be suitable for a courtyard garden?
- What is the difference between perennial and annual flowers?
- What species of shrubbery might be suitable for a courtyard garden?

SOURCE LINK

- To review the use of spreadsheets in financial transactions, refer to the Source Book Chapter 4: Personal Finance. If you need help to format spreadsheets, see Utility 31.

Landscape Gardening

- What might be an appealing name and logo for a landscape gardening company?

Visit a local garden shop to research types and prices of flowers, shrubs, and trees. Obtain information on techniques for planting lawns, flowers, shrubs, and trees.

GETTING STARTED

The plan on the following page shows an area to be landscaped at a university residence. To calculate costs for material and labour, complete exercises 1 to 6. In exercise 7, construct and use a spreadsheet to summarize these costs.

1. To discourage weeds, the flower beds may be lined with landscape fabric over which mulch is placed to a depth of 5 cm. Estimate the area and the cost, if the landscape fabric is bought in rolls and costs 50¢/m^2, and the mulch, bought in bulk, costs \$10/m^3.

2. The lawn area requires a base of topsoil 10-cm deep. The flower beds by the side of the building are 50 cm deep. The rockery garden is built up to a height of 1 m. Each tree requires a hole 1 m in diameter and 1 m deep. Each roughly cylindrical hole is filled with topsoil. The cedar hedging, bamboo, and rhododendron bushes require holes 50 cm in diameter and 50 cm deep. These holes are filled with topsoil. The boxwood hedging requires a trench approximately 50 cm wide and 50 cm deep. Topsoil can be purchased for \$15/m^3. Estimate the volume and cost of the topsoil required for the garden.

3. The lawn seed may be purchased for \$15 per 2-kg bag. Each bag covers 100 m^2. Estimate the number of bags of seed required and the cost.

4. The table lists the wholesale price for items needed to complete the garden.

Item	Price
Rhododendron	\$25 each
Bamboo	\$10 each
Cedar hedging	\$8 each
Boxwood hedging	\$6 each
Japanese maple	\$60 each
Willow	\$45 each
Bedding plants	\$8 per dozen
Water lilies	\$6 each
Rockery rocks (250-cm^2 base)	\$5 each
Rockery rocks (1-m^2 base)	\$20 each
Paving stones (1 m × 1 m)	\$6 each
Shale paving (0.5-m^2 base)	\$6 each
Pond pump	\$250 each

Estimate the total cost for these items if the cedar hedge requires 1 plant every metre, the boxwood requires 1 plant every 50 cm, and the bedding plants need to be planted approximately 25 cm apart. Approximately 75 small and 20 large rockery rocks are needed for the rockery garden and the pond. Assume the budget for all plants on this list is $1500. Adjust the distribution of the plants to stay within this budget.

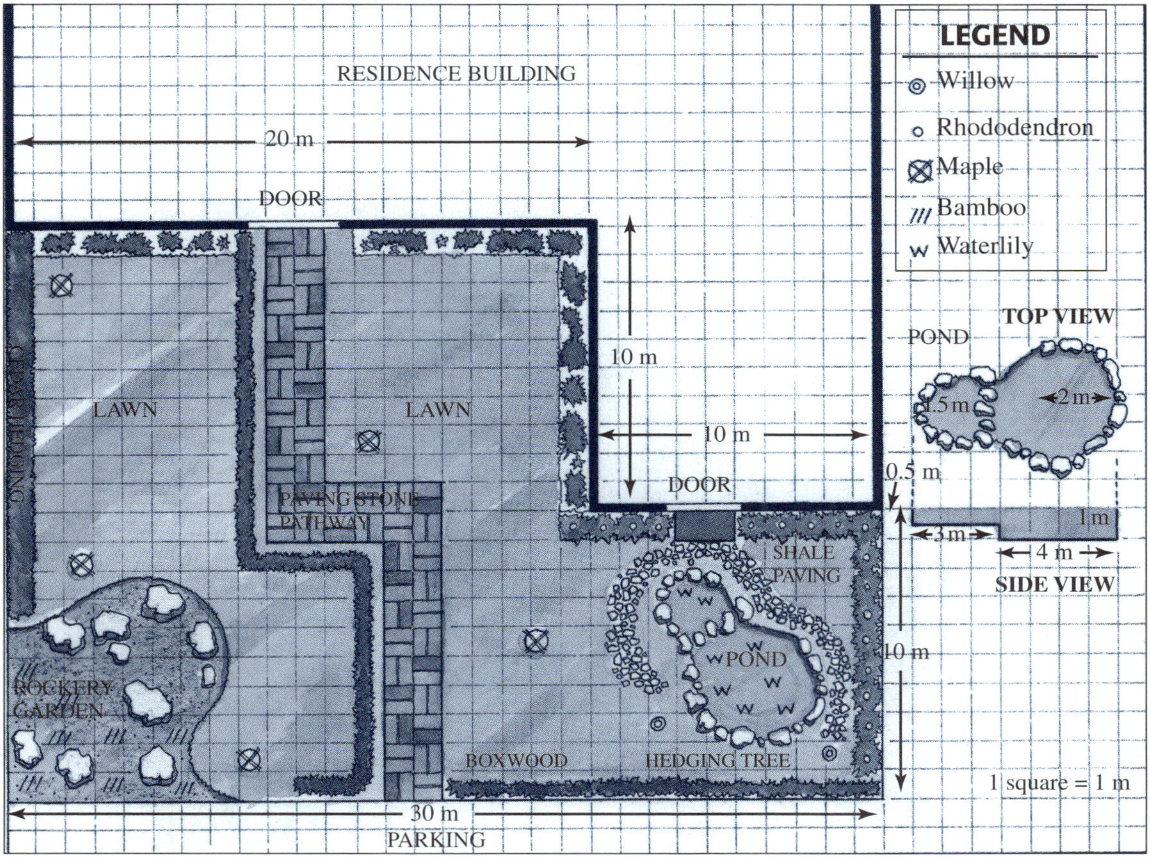

5. The plan shows the top and side views of the pond. Estimate the cost to waterproof the pond if the material costs $8/m^2$. Estimate the volume of water needed to fill the pond.

6. The labour costs for the project include $100/h for design and consulting fees, $45/h for the pond technician, and $15/h for the gardener. The project requires 20 h of design and consulting work, 50 h for pond construction, 40 h of garden layout, and 2 gardeners working together. Determine the labour costs for each person and the total labour costs.

Landscape Gardening

7. Consider the invoice for landscaping the garden.

WESTERN LANDSCAPING LTD.

	A	B	C	D	E	F	G	H	I
1	Material	Costs				Labour	Costs		
2									
3	Item	Quantity	Unit Cost	Total Cost		Labour Details	Hours	Rate	Total
4									
5	Topsoil					Gardeners			
6	Landscape Fabric					Pond Technician			
7	Small Rocks					Design			
8	Large Rocks								
9	Pond Liner								
10	Pond Pump								
11	Paving (1 × 1)								
12	Shale Paving								
13	Fertilizer								
14	Maple Tree								
15	Willow Tree								
16	Rhododendron					Total Materials			
17	Boxwood					Total Labour			
18	Cedar Hedging					Subtotal			
19	Bedding Plants					GST @ 7%			
20	Lawn Seed					PST @ 7%			
21	Bamboo					Total Taxes			
22	Mulch					TOTAL			

In the spreadsheet program:

a) What formula goes in cell D5? Into which cells is it copied?

b) What formula goes in cell I5? Into which cells is it copied?

c) What formula must go in cell I16?

d) What formula must go in cell I17?

e) What formulas must go in cells I18, I19, I20, I21, and I22 respectively?

f) How might you adapt the formula in cell I20 if you were in a province with 6% PST?

PROJECT PRESENTATION

Use what you learned in Getting Started to complete your project. You might modify some techniques, such as substituting sod for grass seed, or wood chips for the surface of the rockery. Your project will include the following items.

- Detailed plans for a garden – use the area given in Getting Started, or choose your area
- Estimates, itemized lists, and total costs for all materials and labour, based on the landscape artist's design
- A spreadsheet for an invoice that details these costs

Here is a description of each person's responsibilities.

Landscape Designer: Design a garden for a condominium complex, apartment building, or university residence. Your plans will show the dimensions and locations of the flower beds, and the types and locations of trees, shrubs, and flowers to be planted. The plans will show the shapes, sizes, and locations of ponds or waterfalls, and all lawn areas, pathways, and other features such as rockeries, benches, and fences.

Financial Advisor: Work with the landscape artist to itemize and calculate the costs for all plants and materials required for the garden. Estimate the costs for labour and creative design. Develop a spreadsheet to calculate the totals and allows you to input your own figures. The spreadsheet will include a company name and logo.

Career Opportunities

There are opportunities in landscape design for workers with a variety of talents. An interest in plants and knowledge of horticulture combined with spatial awareness and design skills are necessary for the development of landscape projects. Marketing of these projects requires presentation skills as well as expertise in computing and administration.

House Building Costs

Suggested Group Size: 1 or 2

Materials: Real estate sections from newspapers, real estate magazines, computer with a spreadsheet program; Internet access (optional)

THE TASK

In this project, you will create a spreadsheet template that allows the user to estimate the total cost and monthly financing costs for a variety of home building options.

BACKGROUND

The choice of a home is one of the most important decisions a person makes. Many people would like their home to reflect their individual taste, but cannot afford the cost of custom building. From the developer's point of view, uniformity allows bulk purchase of materials and economies of scale. To satisfy these opposing objectives, developers of new subdivisions typically offer some variety in lot size and model design. For any model, there are usually optional upgrades in fittings and decoration. Upgrades may include finished recreation rooms, hardwood floors, paved driveways, landscaping, and so on.

Here are some questions to consider.

- What aspects of a home are most important?
- What ranges of price and house model are offered in subdivisions in your community?
- What is the price range of upgrades offered in subdivisions in your community?
- What is the mill rate in your community? What are typical property taxes?
- What is the effect of a longer, rather than a shorter, term for a mortgage?

SOURCE LINK

- For a review of compound interest and the use of spreadsheets in financial transactions, refer to the Source Book, Chapter 4: Personal Finance. If you need help to format spreadsheets, see Utility 31.

House Building Costs

- Think of a building contractor who develops a new neighbourhood. If the neighbourhood offers 4 lot sizes, and 6 different house models with 5 upgrade options for each, how many different types of property are available?

GETTING STARTED

A spreadsheet template can be a useful tool for the contractor and his or her customers. The template should have built-in functions to simplify its use. The spreadsheet should allow the contractor to input choice of lot size, house model, and upgrade options. It will then calculate the total price of the home. To make a spreadsheet for this purpose, it is convenient to use IF functions.

An IF function uses the following syntax:

=IF(condition,then,else)

1. Suppose =IF(B3="*",1000,0) were entered in cell B6. The computer's response would be to look in B3. If there were an * in B3, it would print 1000 in the active cell, cell B6. Otherwise, it would print 0 in B6. What action would the computer execute in cell C6 if the function is =IF(C5="*",2000,10) and

a) there is an asterisk in C5?

b) there is no entry in C5?

2. IF functions can also be nested within one another. That is, the function can apply to more than one set of alternatives. What actions would the computer execute under the following conditions on reading this function in cell B6?
=IF(B3 ="*",100,IF(B2="*",200,0))

a) There is an * in B3.

b) There is no * in B3, but there is an * in B2.

c) There are no entries in B3 or B2.

3. What actions would the computer execute under the following conditions on reading this function in cell B6?
=IF(B1="*",100,IF(B2="*",200,IF(B3="*",300,0)))

a) There is an * in B1.

b) There is an * in B2.

c) There is an * in B3.

d) There are no entries in B1, B2, or B3.

4. Create a spreadsheet called House Price Estimator. Set it up so that prospective customers select which lot, house, and upgrade option(s) they want by entering an * in appropriate cells. An example is shown below for the first section of the spreadsheet, the choice of a lot.

	A	B	C	D	E	F
1	**House Price Estimator**					
2	Enter * beside your choice					
3						
4	**Lot Selection**					
5	Lot Type	Price $	Taxes $/year	Choice *	Subtotals	Taxes
6	a) 55 x 110 corner lot	35000	350			
7	b) 65 x 100 lot	42000	350			
8	c) "estate area" lot	55000	500			
9	Lot Subtotal					
10	Lot Taxes					
11						

a) What formula should be entered in cell E9 to specify the subtotal for the lot choice?

b) What formula should be entered in cell F10 to specify the taxes due on the lot chosen?

5. Homebuyers bring individual needs and resources to the purchase. Factors that may vary are amount of down payment, interest rate available for a mortgage, and term of the finance agreement. Add a section for financing to your spreadsheet. It should include cells for the prospective customer to enter the down payment, desired mortgage term, and annual interest rate. You have used the PMT function with the TI-83 TVM solver. Use the Help menu to review the use of the PMT function with a spreadsheet.

Consider a house with a purchase price of $156 200 and a down payment of $50 000. Mortgage payments are due at the end of each month.

House Building Costs

a) Set up the spreadsheet below to calculate the monthly payment (PMT) required on the mortgage

i) for 25 years at 7%.

ii) for 20 years at 8.25%.

What formula would you enter in cell B33? B37? B38?

b) For each set of conditions, set up the spreadsheet to calculate the monthly PIT (Payment including Interest and Taxes) if property taxes are estimated to be $1960 per year. What formula would you enter in B41? B42?

	A	B	C
29			
30	**FINANCING**		
31	Total Home Cost	156,200	
32	Down Payment	50,000	
33	Mortgage Amount Required		
34	Mortgage term (years)	25	
35	Annual interest rate (%)	7%/12	
36	Payments per year	12	
37	nper		
38	PMT		
39			
40	Property Taxes	1960	
41	Monthly property taxes		
42	Monthly PIT		
43			

PROJECT PRESENTATION

Plan a subdivision with a choice of 3 lot sizes, 4 house models, and 3 upgrade options for each model. Use what you learned in Getting Started to set up your House Price Estimator spreadsheet to calculate the total cost of a house in your subdivision. Assign names and values for lot sizes, model types, upgrades, and taxes. Provide a calculation for total home cost and total yearly property taxes. Incorporate a financing section into the spreadsheet to allow calculation of monthly PIT.

A New Home

Your completed project will include the following.

- A plan and map of the neighbourhood
- Descriptions of the choices available for lot size, house models, and upgrade options
- A handwritten plan of your spreadsheet to be submitted ***before*** the spreadsheet is created on the computer
- A complete spreadsheet, with categories for lot, house, and upgrade options and calculations for total home cost, total yearly property taxes, and monthly PIT
- A copy of the spreadsheet on which formulas are shown
- A sales brochure

Here is a description of your responsibilities.

Planner: Create a plan for the development. Draw a map of the neighbourhood and illustrate streets, shopping centres, and parks. Include a written description of your design. Set up the House Price Estimator section of the spreadsheet.

Real-Estate Salesperson: Create a sales brochure to demonstrate options for lot size, house model, and upgrades. Describe how you will match a buyer and the best option. Set up the financing section of the spreadsheet.

Career Opportunities

The housing industry offers many opportunities. Detail-oriented individuals with computer skills are in demand as project managers and real estate salespeople. Design and computer skills are needed in advance planning of developments.

Surviving on the Ocean's Shore

Suggested Group Size: 2

Materials: Graphing calculator, grid paper, Internet access (optional)

THE TASK

In this project, you will study tides and how changes in water level can be represented mathematically. You will use sinusoidal functions and their applications and develop mathematical models to predict tide levels. You will also study the environment of the tidal zones.

BACKGROUND

Life on the ocean's shore is challenging, especially for plants and animals exposed to the effects of tide. Tide is the movement of ocean water that results from the gravitational pull of the moon. During part of a normal day, the tide will cause water levels to rise to a maximum (called high tide) and fall to a minimum (called low tide).

The area that lies between high and low tide levels, called the inter-tidal zone, is exposed to seawater and then to air, repeatedly. The wide variety of plants and animals that inhabit this zone must be adapted to constantly changing conditions. This vibrant, vital ecosystem is extremely important to the world's environment, but it is also very susceptible to the effects of pollution.

The careful analysis of environmental factors such as tide change can produce mathematical models useful in determining the health of our planet. You will study the inter-tidal zone and use a graphing calculator to predict water levels at various times of the day.

SOURCE LINK

- For a review of sinusoidal graphs, refer to the Source Book, Chapter 5: Sinusoidal Data. If you need help to use sine regression on the TI-83, see Utility 32.

Surviving
on the Ocean's Shore

Consider the part of the ocean shore that is under water when the tide is high, yet is dry when the tide is low.

- What sort of changes in temperature, light, and water content might one expect in these areas?
- What types of animals live on the shore or under the sand near the shore?
- How might animals adapt to the rapidly changing environment created by tides?
- How might animals and plants that exist in the inter-tidal zone be affected by sunlight and by waves?
- How might sedentary animals that are out of water for only a few hours adapt?
- What forms of pollution might be seen on the ocean's shoreline?

Granville Island, Vancouver

GETTING STARTED

1. The following data on sea level and time were collected at a harbour near Vancouver, British Columbia.

Time (h) (0 is midnight)	Sea level (feet)
0	2.1
1	2.8
2	3.3
3	3.6
4	3.6
5	3.3
6	2.8
7	2.1
8	1.4
9	0.9
10	0.6
11	0.6
12	0.9

2. Plot the data on a scatterplot. Connect the points and observe the shape of the graph. At what time is high tide? What is the amplitude of the function? What does amplitude mean in terms of sea level?

3. Determine the equation of the sinusoidal curve of best fit for the data in exercise 1. Graph the function and ensure you are able to see one complete cycle of tide movement. Use the TRACE feature to predict the time of the next high and low tides.

4. Use the function from exercise 3 to estimate the amplitude, period, and maximum and minimum sea level.

5. Places located away from Vancouver will experience high and low tides either later or earlier in the day. Tides also vary in their intensity based on the geographic features of the area. Describe how the function you found could be adjusted to predict the tides for other locations.

Surviving on the Ocean's Shore

PROJECT PRESENTATION

Use what you learned in Getting Started to begin your project. Your group will analyze the tide levels at 2 locations. The information is necessary to determine the effect of tidal flows on wildlife in the inter-tidal zone. Your completed project will include the following.

- A description of the shorelines selected for study
- Labelled graphs of the change in sea level over a period of time for the 2 locations
- A description of the functions that generated the graphs
- An explanation of any differences found between the 2 locations
- A description, or graphs, of conditions at 3 points within the inter-tidal zone (low, mid, and high tide level) for each location
- Information on the adaptations of 2 animals that live in the inter-tidal zone

Here are detailed descriptions of each person's responsibilities.

Oceanographer: Select 2 ocean-side locations where data on water levels can be collected throughout a typical day. Ensure that the locations are different in topography. You might use the Internet to search under the key words "tide tables." Enter the data into a graphing calculator (use lists L1 to L4 on the TI-83). Determine the sinusoidal functions that best describe the data sets. Graph the functions and use the graphs as a guide when you write your report. For each location:

- Describe water levels at 1-h intervals during a typical 12-h period.
- Describe, or graph, conditions at points on the shoreline located near the low, mid, and high tide marks.

Note any differences you notice between the 2 locations.

Marine Biologist: Research the types of animals and plants that live in the inter-tidal zone of the shore in the locations selected by the Oceanographer. Examine the survival strategies of different species. Compare the adaptations necessary for life at low, mid, and high tide levels. Select an animal that maintains its position as the tide moves (such as an oyster) and investigate its adaptations to underwater and exposed environments. Use the function found by the Oceanographer as the basis to write a report on "A Day in the Life of the _______."

Career Opportunities

People interested in Marine Sciences work for the government, private companies, and environmental concerns. Often, they work out of doors to gather samples and data. Careers in the technical and applied side of Marine Sciences require an understanding of physics, mathematics, and biology.

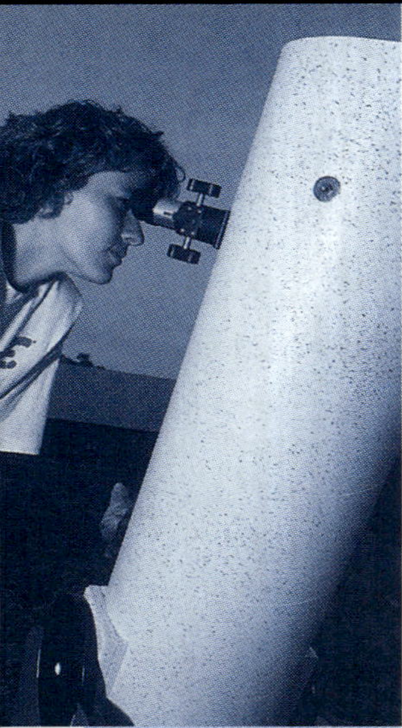

Sun, Moon, and Stars

Suggested Group Size: 4

Materials: Grid paper, poster paper, a large styrofoam ball, pins with coloured heads, felt markers, a protractor, compasses, a white card, a straw, thread, a washer; a tripod, a model of a celestial sphere, Internet access (optional)

THE TASK

In this project, you will create posters, graphs, and a model of the celestial sphere to illustrate the apparent motion of the sun, moon, and stars as viewed from Earth. You will build an astrolabe to measure the positions of the sun, moon, and stars.

BACKGROUND

Early astronomers observed the heavens with the naked eye or through very simple telescopes. They saw that the sun rose and set at different places and at different times of day as the year proceeded. They saw that the moon and stars also appeared to rise and set over the course of a night, and their relative positions in the sky changed as the seasons changed. From their observations, astronomers developed theories about the universe. Clocks and calendars were devised based on astronomical records, and explorers used the positions of the sun, moon, and stars to help them navigate. Modern day astronomers use high-tech telescopes and computers to collect and analyze data.

- Review the relationships of a day, a month, and a year to the movement of the earth and the moon within the solar system.
- Can you locate the Big Dipper constellation and the North Star? What other stars and constellations do you recognize?
- What are the names of the constellations of the zodiac? Research their positions relative to the path of the sun.
- Research *vernal equinox*, *autumnal equinox*, *summer solstice*, and *winter solstice*. On what dates do these occur?
- What is the meaning of *ecliptic*?
- What are the latitude and longitude of your city or town?

SOURCE LINK

- For a review of sinusoidal data, refer to the Source Book, Chapter 5: Sinusoidal Data. If you need help to use sine regression on the TI-83, see Utility 32.

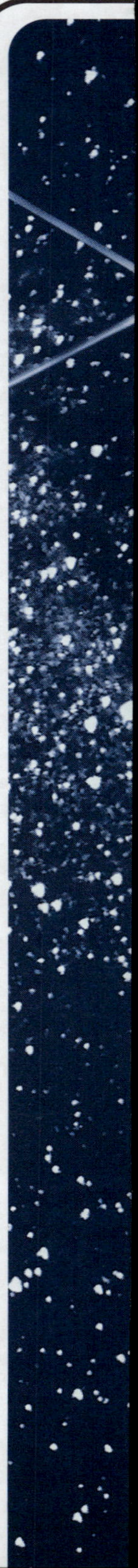

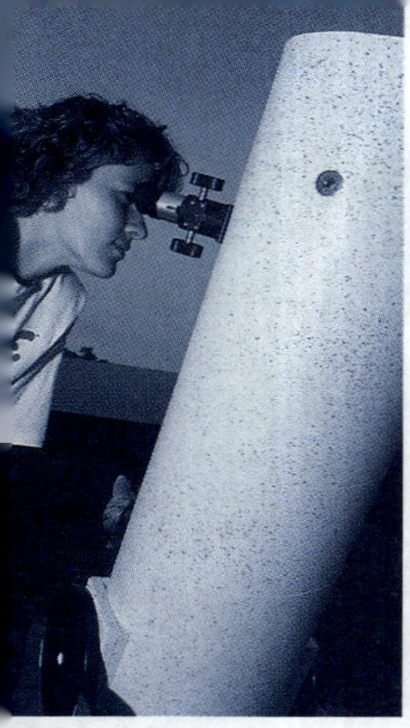

Sun, Moon, and Stars

GETTING STARTED

The angle made by the line of sight of an object in the sky and the horizon is called the *altitude* of the object. The altitude of a star depends upon the location of the observer on Earth.

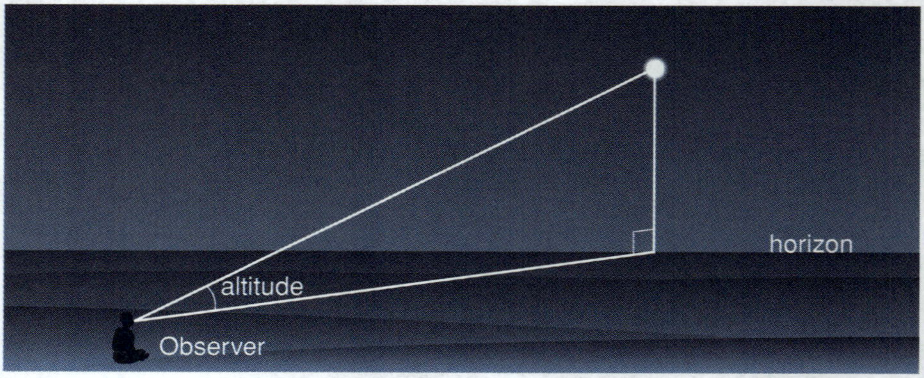

As a group, build an *astrolabe*, similar to the one in the diagram below, to take readings of the altitude of the sun, moon, and stars. If possible, use a tripod when you take the readings.

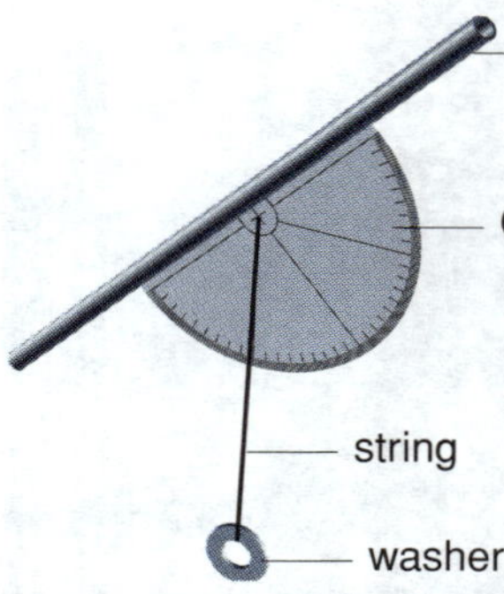

1. a) Go outside on a clear night and locate the Big Dipper and the North Star (Polaris). Take a reading of the altitude of the end "pointer star" of the Big Dipper and the altitude of Polaris. Return to the same viewing spot 2 or 3 hours later and note the altitudes again.

b) Compare the two readings of the altitude of the pointer star.

c) Compare the two readings of the altitude of Polaris.

d) Relate the altitude of Polaris to the latitude of your community.

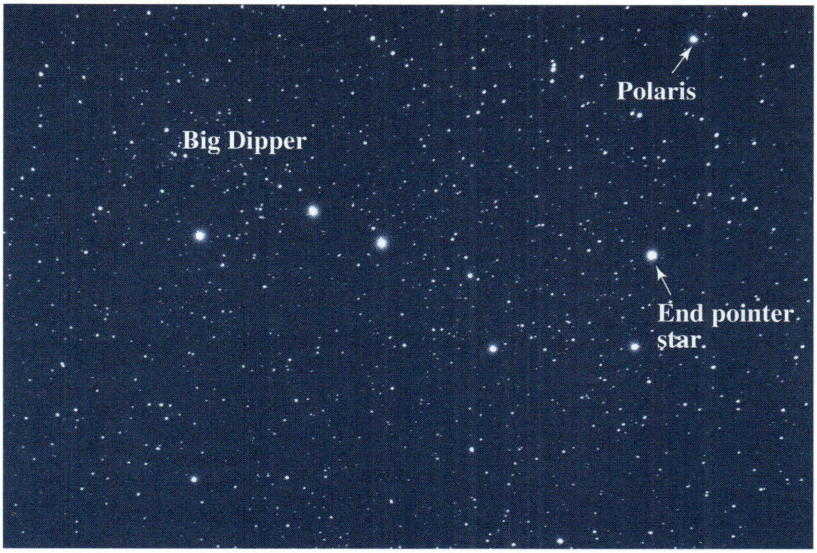

2. a) Use your astrolabe outside on a clear sunny day to take hourly readings of the altitude of the sun. **DO NOT LOOK DIRECTLY** through the straw sight into the sun as this will cause permanent damage to your eyes. Position a piece of card over the end of the straw sight to throw a shadow on a screen placed behind the astrolabe. Arrange the card and screen as shown in the diagram. Adjust the angle of the astrolabe so that the sun's projected image is a clear bright circle in the centre of the shadow formed on the screen.

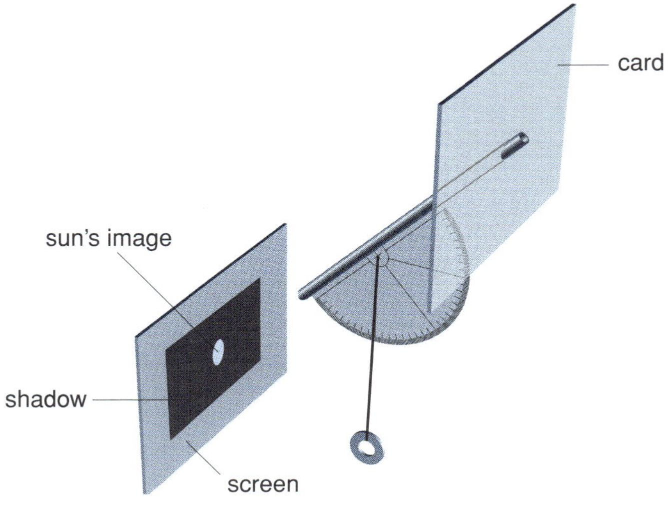

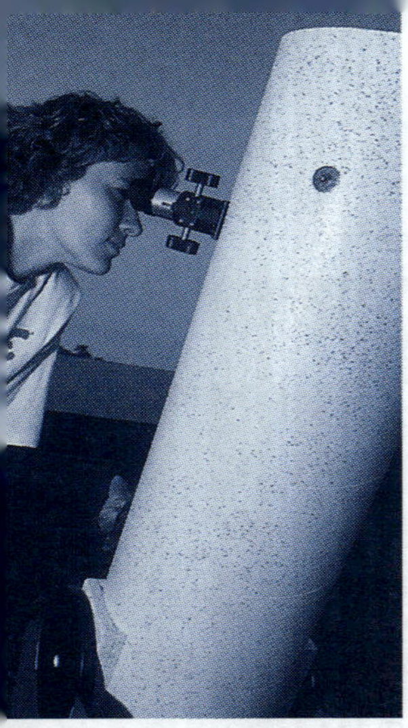

Sun, Moon, and Stars

Any clear day is suitable, but one of the equinoxes or solstices is most interesting. Try to obtain as many readings as possible for that day. Record your readings in a table like the one below. These data were obtained from the Internet. If you cannot obtain readings yourself, use these data.

Altitude of the Sun at W 120°, N 50°
March 21, 2000

Time (PST)	Altitude (degrees)
05:00	–10.3
06:00	–0.8
07:00	9.0
08:00	18.2
09:00	26.6
10:00	33.7
11:00	38.6
12:00	40.6
13:00	39.4
14:00	35.1
15:00	28.5
16:00	20.3
17:00	11.3
18:00	2.0
19:00	–7.9

Source: U.S. Naval Observatory

b) Use your graphing calculator to plot a graph with time of day (0 to 24 h) on the horizontal axis and altitude on the vertical axis (from –60° to 60°).

c) Find the equation of the sinusoidal regression for your data. Give your answer for the equation correct to two decimal places. With Plot Off, graph this equation. Plot the sinusoidal regression curve from 0 to 24 h on grid paper.

d) Use your calculator to determine the times of sunrise, sunset, and maximum altitude. Mark these times on your graph.

Celestial objects appear to change position from day to day due to the movement of Earth. The positions of the sun, moon, and stars at any time can be mapped onto what astronomers call the *celestial sphere*. The celestial sphere is an imagined full sphere that surrounds Earth, rather like a planetarium screen. It has a *celestial equator*, a *celestial north* and *south pole*, and lines of *celestial latitude* and *longitude*. The celestial sphere provides a coordinate system that enables scientists to locate objects in the sky accurately. It provides a frame of reference on which to describe the motions of the sun, moon, and stars as they appear to move across the sky.

The *angle of declination* is the angle an object makes with the *celestial equator*. It does not depend upon the location of the observer. The *angle of declination* is 0° at the equator, 90° at the north celestial pole, and -90° at the south celestial pole. *Angles of declination* are similar to degrees of latitude on a globe of Earth.

East–West measurements are made along the celestial equator and are called *right ascension*. They are similar to degrees of longitude on a globe. The point with *right ascension* 0° and *declination* 0°, (0, 0), is the point at which the path of the sun crosses the celestial equator on the *vernal equinox* (March 21). This is called the *first point of Aries*.

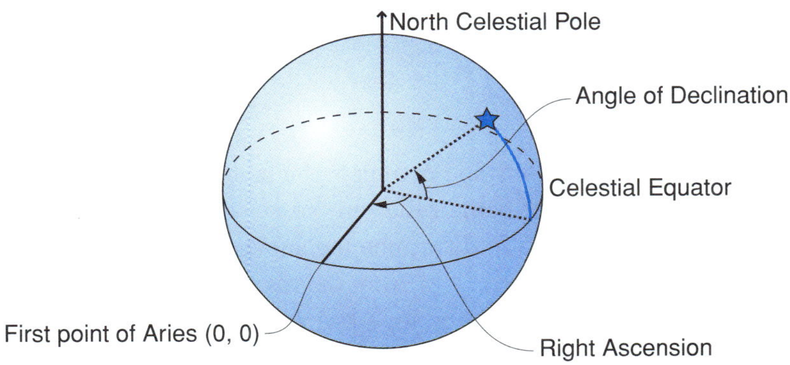

3. The *ecliptic* is the apparent annual path of the sun across the celestial sphere. Plot the *ecliptic* over the course of a year, with the *angle of right ascension* on the horizontal axis and the *angle of declination* on the vertical axis. Your plot will be on a rectangular grid. This grid, like a map of Earth, is a projection of a sphere onto a two-dimensional surface.

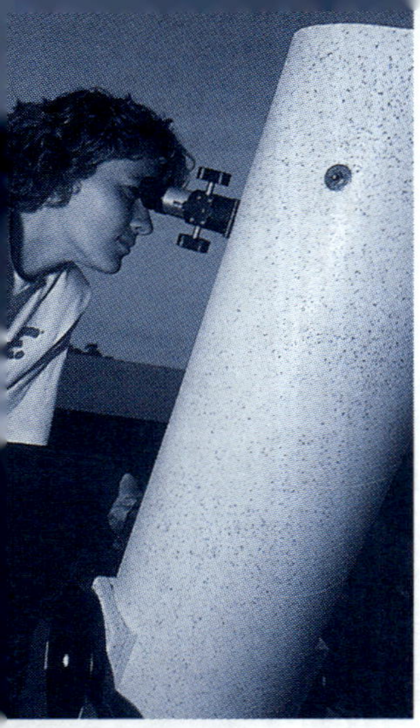

Sun, Moon, and Stars

a) Complete the table to convert dates to day numbers. Consider March 21, the *vernal equinox*, as day 0; March 31 will be day 10; April 1 will be day 11; and April 21 will be day 31. The *summer solstice*, on June 21, will be day 92.

Date	Mar. 21	Apr. 21	May 21	June 21	July 21	Aug. 21	Sept. 21	Oct. 21	Nov. 21	Dec. 21	Jan. 21	Feb. 21
Day #	0	31		92								

The sun appears to move approximately 1° per day (approximately 360° in one year), so you may use the entries for day number as entries for *right ascension*.

The table below shows the sun's maximum altitude (in degrees) at monthly intervals over one year in Windsor, Ontario, at latitude 42° N.

Date	Mar. 21	Apr. 21	May 21	June 21	July 21	Aug. 21	Sept. 21	Oct. 21	Nov. 21	Dec. 21	Jan. 21	Feb. 21
Right Ascension	0	31		92								
Maximum Altitude (°)	48	60	68	71	68	60	49	37	28	25	28	37
Declination Angle (°)	0	12										

b) Copy and complete the table above. At the vernal equinox (March 21), the path of the sun crosses the equator, so the angle of declination is 0°. To determine the angle of declination for each date in the table, subtract 48° from the maximum altitude. For example, the angle of declination for April 21 will be $60° - 48° = 12°$ and for October 21 will be $37° - 48° = -11°$.

c) Use your calculator to plot the graph for angles of declination between −40° and 40°.

d) Use your calculator to find the sinusoidal regression equation for these data. With Plot Off, graph this equation. Use the graph to determine the angle of declination of the sun for each date.

i) January 1 **ii)** your birthday

e) Use your calculator to find the maximum and minimum angles of declination of the sun, and the dates when these occur. What do you notice about these dates?

f) Use your calculator to find the date(s) when the angle of declination of the sun is 10°.

g) Plot the graph on grid paper. On the graph, mark the points found in parts d and e.

4. Construct a model of the celestial sphere on a large Styrofoam ball. Draw the equator and mark off points every 15°. Label points every 30°. Draw the circle of longitude, which passes through the first point of Aries (0, 0). Mark off points along this circle every 15° and label points every 30°.

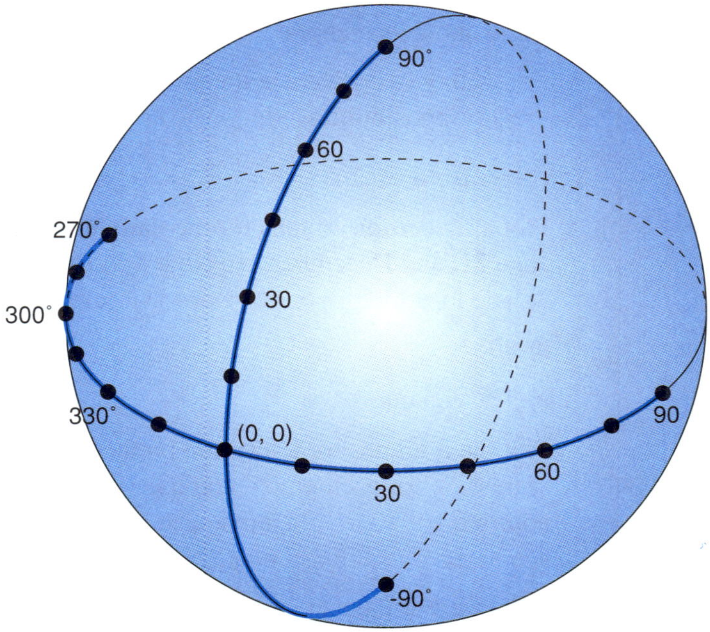

PROJECT PRESENTATION

Use what you learned in Getting Started to extend your project. Incorporate diagrams, pictures, data tables, all graphs, and brief definitions of key terms and ideas. Use graphing calculators and transfer graphs onto grid paper for display on posters. If possible, use the Internet to obtain your own data on the positions of the sun, moon, and stars. Alternatively, use the data sheets included at the end of this project.

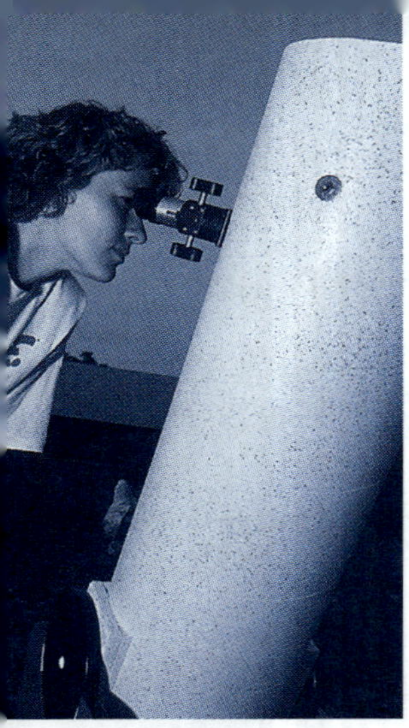

Sun, Moon, and Stars

Your project will include the following:

- Data and associated graphs from any observations you made using an astrolabe
- A poster on the apparent motion of the sun
- A poster on the motion and phases of the moon as viewed from Earth
- A model of the celestial sphere to display the paths of the sun and various stars over 1 year
- A two-dimensional projection of the celestial sphere onto a rectangular grid to show the ecliptic and the positions of the zodiac constellations

Work together to coordinate the project. Here is a description of each person's responsibilities.

Sun Researchers (2):

a) Plot altitude/time graphs for the daily motion of the sun for March 21, June 21, and December 21, as viewed from each position.

  i) The location of your city or town (or from 50° N)

  ii) 80° N

  iii) The equator

Plot the 3 graphs for a location on the same axes. Find the sinusoidal regression for each graph, and use your calculator to determine the approximate times of sunrise and sunset and the maximum altitude of the sun at the 3 locations on each of these dates.

> **Note:** For the equator data, parts of the sinusoidal regression graphs may not be realistic. Why?

b) Write a description of the differences between the apparent motion of the sun on these dates at the equator, in the arctic, and at your own location. Compare the duration of daylight and the maximum altitude of the sun at the 3 locations on each of the dates.

c) Create a poster on the apparent motion of the sun. Include the work from exercise 3 of Getting Started.

Moon Researcher (1):

a) To investigate the moon's motion, record its altitude at the *same time* every evening for 1 month. Plot an altitude/time graph for these data. Find the sinusoidal regression equation for these data and graph this equation. Estimate the dates when the moon is at the horizon. On which of these dates is the moon rising?

b) Plot a graph of the percent illumination of the moon versus day of the month. Find the sinusoidal regression equation for these data and graph this equation. Predict the approximate dates for full moon and new moon for the month you chose and for the following month.

c) Plot an altitude/time graph for the motion of the moon over the course of one day. Find the sinusoidal regression equation for these data and graph this equation. Estimate the times when the moon rises and sets, and the maximum altitude on the day you chose and on the next day.

d) Create a poster on the motion and phases of the moon.

Constellations Researcher (1):

a) Construct a model of the celestial sphere and mark the ecliptic on it.

b) Research the positions of the constellations in the zodiac. Use coloured pins to represent the constellations on your model.

c) Write definitions of the following key terms: *astrolabe*, *altitude*, *declination*, *right ascension*, *celestial sphere*, *vernal equinox*, *autumnal equinox*, *winter solstice*, *summer solstice*, *ecliptic*, *first point of Aries*. Where possible, illustrate your definitions with diagrams.

Career Opportunities

Modern astronomers work to increase our understanding of the universe. They need skills in physics and computer science. Skills in data organization and presentation are needed in many fields, such as museum science, television production, and marketing.

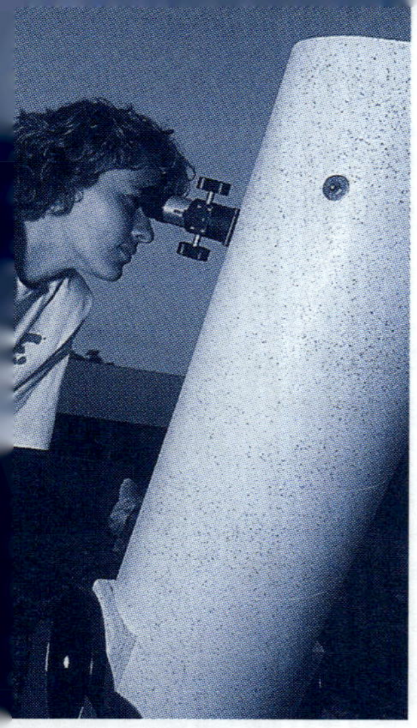

Sun, Moon, and Stars

Sun, Moon and Stars Data Sheets

The data on the following pages have been obtained on the Internet at the U.S. Naval Observatory site. A break in the output table indicates that the object has dropped more than 12° below the horizon and is not near the horizon again until the next indicated time.

Moon Data for Month–January 2000

Adapted from Astronomical Sky Calendar on Electronic Ephemeris www.ifa.hawaii.edu. Also available at bcasey@imagiware.com.

ALTITUDE OF THE SUN (h.m. Pacific Standard Time)

EQUATOR , W120 00, 0 00 Altitude, Mar. 21, 2000		EQUATOR , W120 00, 0 00 Altitude, June 21, 2000		EQUATOR , W120 00, 0 00 Altitude, Dec. 21, 2000	
h.m.	**Altitude (°)**	**h.m.**	**Altitude (°)**	**h.m.**	**Altitude (°)**
06:00	–1.8	06:00	0.1	06:00	0.8
07:00	13.3	07:00	13.4	07:00	14.2
08:00	28.3	08:00	26.9	08:00	27.7
09:00	43.3	09:00	40.1	09:00	40.8
10:00	58.3	10:00	52.3	10:00	52.9
11:00	73.2	11:00	62.2	11:00	62.6
12:00	88.2	12:00	66.6	12:00	66.6
13:00	76.7	13:00	62.7	13:00	62.2
14:00	61.7	14:00	53.0	14:00	52.3
15:00	46.7	15:00	40.9	15:00	40.1
16:00	31.8	16:00	27.8	16:00	27.0
17:00	16.8	17:00	14.2	17:00	13.5
18:00	2.0	18:00	0.9	18:00	0.2

NORTH 50 DEGREES
W120 00, N50 00
Altitude, Mar. 21, 2000

h.m.	Altitude (°)
05:00	–10.3
06:00	–0.8
07:00	9.0
08:00	18.2
09:00	26.6
10:00	33.7
11:00	38.6
12:00	40.6
13:00	39.4
14:00	35.1
15:00	28.5
16:00	20.3
17:00	11.3
18:00	2.0
19:00	–7.9

NORTH 50 DEGREES
W120 00, N50 00
Altitude, June 21, 2000

h.m.	Altitude (°)
03:00	–6.6
04:00	0.8
05:00	8.6
06:00	17.5
07:00	26.9
08:00	36.6
09:00	45.9
10:00	54.4
11:00	60.8
12:00	63.4
13:00	61.1
14:00	54.9
15:00	46.5
16:00	37.2
17:00	27.6
18:00	18.1
19:00	9.1
20:00	1.2
21:00	–6.2
22:00	–11.7

NORTH 50 DEGREES
W120 00, N50 00
Altitude, Dec. 21, 2000

h.m.	Altitude (°)
07:00	–8.5
08:00	0.2
09:00	6.7
10:00	12.1
11:00	15.5
12:00	16.6
13:00	15.4
14:00	11.8
15:00	6.4
16:00	–0.8
17:00	–9.0

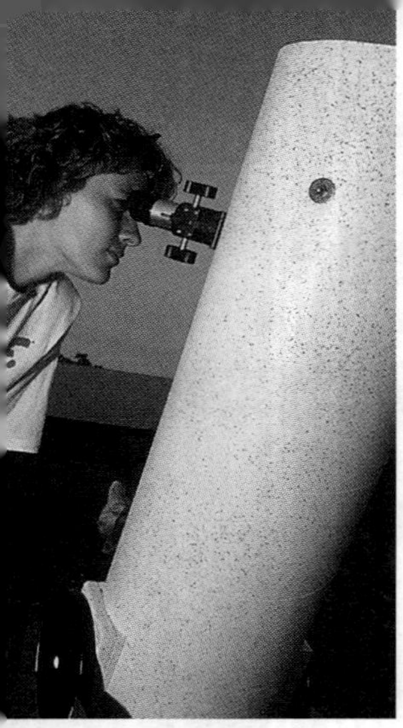

Sun, Moon, and Stars

NORTH 80 DEGREES W120 00, N80 00 Altitude, Mar. 21, 2000		NORTH 80 DEGREES W120 00, N80 00 Altitude, June 21, 2000		NORTH 80 DEGREES W120 00, N80 00 Altitude, Dec. 21, 2000	
h.m.	Altitude (°)	h.m.	Altitude (°)	h.m.	Altitude (°)
00:00	–9.6	00:00	13.5	OBJECT IS	
01:00	–9.3	01:00	13.8	CONTINUOUSLY	
02:00	–8.4	02:00	14.7	BELOW THE HORIZON	
03:00	–6.8	03:00	16.2		
04:00	–4.8	04:00	18.2		
05:00	–2.4	05:00	20.5		
06:00	0.6	06:00	23.0		
07:00	3.0	07:00	25.6		
08:00	5.4	08:00	28.1		
09:00	7.5	09:00	30.3		
10:00	9.2	10:00	32.0		
11:00	10.2	11:00	33.1		
12:00	10.7	12:00	33.5		
13:00	10.4	13:00	33.1		
14:00	9.5	14:00	32.1		
15:00	8.0	15:00	30.4		
16:00	6.0	16:00	28.2		
17:00	3.7	17:00	25.8		
18:00	1.4	18:00	23.2		
19:00	–1.6	19:00	20.6		
20:00	–4.0	20:00	18.3		
21:00	–6.1	21:00	16.3		
22:00	–7.7	22:00	14.8		
23:00	–8.8	23:00	13.8		

ALTITUDE OF THE MOON (h.m. Pacific Standard Time)

50 DEGREES NORTH W120 00, N50 00
Altitude, Mar. 21, 2000

h.m.	Altitude (°)	Fraction Illuminated
00:00	35.8	0.98
01:00	37.6	0.98
02:00	36.3	0.98
03:00	32.3	0.98
04:00	26.0	0.98
05:00	18.2	0.98
06:00	9.5	0.98
07:00	0.5	0.97
08:00	–9.4	0.97
19:00	–11.7	0.96
20:00	–2.5	0.95
21:00	6.6	0.95
22:00	14.9	0.95
23:00	22.3	0.95

MOON DATA - Jan.2000

(local midnight Pacific Daylight Time)

Date	Elevation (°)	% Illumination (expressed as a decimal)
Jan. 1	–14	0.16
2	–17	0.10
3	–19	0.05
4	–21	0.02
5	–21	0.00
6	–21	0.00
7	–19	0.02
8	–17	0.06
9	–14	0.11
10	–11	0.18
11	–7	0.27
12	–2	0.36
13	3	0.47
14	7	0.58
15	12	0.69
16	16	0.79
17	19	0.88
18	21	0.95
19	21	0.99
20	19	1.00
21	16	0.98
22	13	0.93
23	8	0.87
24	4	0.78
25	–1	0.69
26	–5	0.59
27	–9	0.49
28	–13	0.40
29	–16	0.31
30	–19	0.22
31	–20	0.15
Feb. 1	–21	0.09
2	–21	0.04
3	–20	0.01
4	–18	0.00

The Ponzi Scheme

Suggested Group Size: 3

Materials: Grid paper, graphing calculator; spreadsheet and dynamic geometry software, *Ponzipyramid* script, on the *Teacher's Resource Book CD-ROM* (optional)

SOURCE LINK

- To review sequences and fractals, refer to the Source Book, Chapter 6: Patterns. For help with *The Geometer's Sketchpad*, see Utility 23, available from your teacher, or *Applied Mathematics 11, Source Book, Tutorial 6.1*.

THE TASK

In this project, you will simulate and analyze pyramid schemes from the perspective of mathematics and society. You will use technology to generate sequences, graphs, and fractals.

BACKGROUND

Charles Ponzi made, and lost, a fortune in the early 1920s by promoting an investment scheme that was doomed to collapse. The Ponzi scheme is famous as the first of a variety of "get rich quick" pyramid schemes that are illegal for good reason. All pyramid schemes depend on unending growth to sustain them. As soon as the rate of growth starts to decline, the system starts to collapse. All pyramid schemes have a fatal flaw: either limited resources or a limited market. Search the Internet for information on the Ponzi scheme, its collapse, and Ponzi's eventual jail sentence.

Another type of pyramid scheme, the chain letter, usually asks you to pay something to every person on a list, then remove the top name from the list and put your name at the bottom. Assume you receive an "invitation" to send $1 to a list of 6 people and then to continue the chain by sending invitations to 10 friends.

- Would it be better for you to put your name at the top, rather than the bottom, of the list?
- How much would you expect to get back if you sent out 10 invitations? Be realistic!
- If your list of 10 people continue the chain, how might their lists overlap?
- How many people do you think would actually continue the chain?

PONZIIMA.GSP
A
B
Draw Text & Label

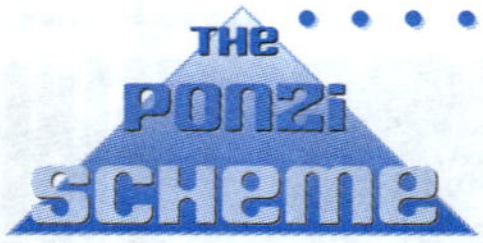

• What do you think are the chances that everyone will make a profit from a chain?

• What do you think are the chances that anyone will make a profit?

Remember: Chain Letters are illegal!

GETTING STARTED

The Club

A partnership of three friends owns a "club" that operates on funds from the sale of memberships and shares. The club offers a service to a maximum of 300 members. To promote membership, a deal is offered. A membership costs $75 and entitles the member to the club services. Members who buy a share in the club for an additional $100 receive 3 free memberships to sell to friends. Members keep the proceeds from the sale of these free memberships.

Analyze **The Club** scenario. Your analysis should demonstrate why such schemes are illegal.

1. **Level 0.** If you and 2 friends were the owners of the club, you would pay $75 membership, and buy a $100 share each. At level 0 the club has a net worth of 3($75 + 100) or $525. As an individual, you have paid $175.

   Level 1. You each recruit 3 friends to buy the free memberships that came with your share purchase. Each of you has made a profit of $50. Explain how this profit was determined. Each of the 9 new members also buys a $100 share in the club. How much is the club worth now? How much profit do the 3 new members earn? How much profit do the original owners make? Assume that every new member buys a share and recruits 3 new members. Record the growth of the club in a spreadsheet or table similar to Table 1.

Table 1

Growth Level (n)	Number of New Members (m)	Total Members (t)	Club Net Worth ($)
0	3	3	525
1	$3 \times 3 = 9$	12	1425
2			
3			

Plot graphs to show how many members are added at each level of growth, the total membership, and the club's net worth.

2. What will happen to the service provided by the club if the number of members exceeds 300? Might people still buy shares just to sell the free memberships and not worry about the service? Assume that many of the members are not interested in the service; they care only about the profit they can make when they sell the memberships. How will this affect the club's assets?

3. Estimate the population of your community and the percent who might join the club. How long would it take to saturate the market; that is, to reach a point where everyone who is interested has already bought a membership? Estimate the total worth of the club at the point when the market is saturated. If you and your 2 original partners were to disband the club and take the money and run, how much money would you have? How many people would have gained financially and by how much? How many people would lose money and how much? What is the ratio of winners to losers? Explain why this kind of scheme is illegal.

4. Explain why the collapse of this scheme is inevitable.

A Geometric Approach: A Fractal Pyramid

Complete this demonstration of some aspects of pyramid schemes. If you have access to *The Geometer's Sketchpad*, ask your teacher for the script entitled *Ponzipyramid* (supplied on the *Teacher's Resource Book CD-ROM*) to perform the construction.

1. **Level 0.** Draw a straight line segment across the bottom of a piece of paper. Measure the length of the line. At level 0, you have 1 segment of length l.

2. **Level 1.** Divide the line into 3 equal segments. On the middle segment, construct a square such that the middle segment is the bottom of the square. What is the area of the square? You have 5 line segments on the top side of the pyramid-to-be. What is the length of each segment? What is the top perimeter?

3. **Level 2.** On each of the 5 segments, repeat the construction from part 2. How many segments are there in level 2? What is the length of each segment? What is the total area of the large and small squares? What is the top perimeter?

THE PONZI SCHEME

4. Repeat the construction. Record the values for each level of detail in a spreadsheet or a table similar to Table 2.

Table 2

Level	Number of Segments	Length of Each Segment	Total Area of Squares	Top Perimeter
0	1	l	0	l
1	5	$l \div 3 =$	$(l \div 3)^2 =$	$5(l \div 3) =$
2				
3				

5. From the table, note any patterns that occur. Use formulas to describe the patterns. Extend the patterns for many more levels in the table. At what level is it too difficult to actually make the construction?

The Power of Compounding

1. There are legal ways to make money through investment, though they may take patience and/or carry risk. Consider an investment of $200. Choose a safe, guaranteed investment vehicle, such as Canada Savings Bonds. Research the current annual compound interest rate. For each year from now until you reach age 65, calculate the value of the compounded investment. Display it in a table and on a graph.

2. Add an additional $60 per year and make a similar table and graph for your investment.

3. Draw a chart for each set of investment data. Draw a line 2.0 cm long to represent the initial $200. For each year, draw another line (to the same scale and centred on the first line) below the previous line to represent the new value of the investment. This is a legal investment pyramid. Label the pyramids and comment on the difference in their shapes.

PROJECT PRESENTATION

Use what you learned in Getting Started to complete your project. Your completed project will consist of a portfolio that includes several items to explain why one should not invest in any pyramid or chain scheme, and why one should look closely at any investment program. Include the following.

- A letter to a friend to explain why an investment in **The Club** is not wise
- A clear statement about the financial prospects of **The Club** (Support your statement by documentation from your analysis of **The Club**.)
- An analysis of a chain letter scheme, supported by data and graphs
- A labelled set of fractal pyramids (Include numeric data and a description of how fractals relate to pyramid or chain schemes.)
- A set of labelled investment growth tables and pyramids related to compound interest, and a description of why this legitimate approach is successful

Here is a detailed description of each person's responsibilities.

Financial Analyst: Analyze financial growth expectations over the short and long term for various scenarios. Clarify who might benefit and who might lose. Draft a statement of the financial prospects for each scenario.

Legal Advisor: Assist with data development. Clarify issues of ethics related to who wins, who loses, the right of the buyer to full disclosure of the scheme, fairness of the scheme, and so on. Draft a letter to advise against investing in a pyramid or chain scheme. Prepare a statement about the societal damage such schemes may cause.

Graphics Designer: Design, prepare, and label tables, charts, and graphs. Show clearly the levels of growth in the different scenarios, and illustrate where difficulties or fallacies exist.

Career Opportunities

In any career, and in life, wise decision making comes from careful analysis of situations. Analysis may take many forms. Careers in the financial or legal professions require people with the skills to analyze the details of various business ventures to ensure that they are financially sound and legal.

Threatened and Endangered species

Suggested Group Size: 2

Materials: Grid paper, a graphing calculator; access to a computer with a spreadsheet program, Internet access (optional)

THE TASK

In this project, you will produce a pamphlet or a web site about an endangered animal species. The purpose of the pamphlet or web site is to increase public awareness of the species and the steps being taken to preserve it. You will use technology to generate and graph sequences that model the population of the species. The graphs will be included in the pamphlet or web site.

BACKGROUND

In 2000, there were over one thousand threatened or endangered species of animals worldwide. The decline in the populations of many species of animals (and plants) during the last century is a major concern. Many animal species have come to the brink of extinction due to factors such as climate changes, loss of habitat, hunting, pesticide use, and general encroachment by humans. There has been a huge effort to save endangered animals through a ban on hunting, preservation of wildlife habitat, and the development of breeding programs. Biologists who work for government agencies, zoos, and conservation groups study the population growth patterns of endangered species in the wild, in protected areas, and in specialized breeding programs. In these ways, scientists can assess and predict the current and future status of the species. Animals such as the mountain gorilla, the African elephant, the whooping crane, and several species of whale, are now slowly making a comeback. Much work remains to be done worldwide to ensure that the biological diversity of our planet is sustained.

SOURCE LINK

- To review sequences, refer to the Source Book, Chapter 6: Patterns, *Tutorials 6.1* and *6.2*. If you wish to graph sequences on the TI-83, see Utility 33.

Threatened and Endangered

species

- List some species that are endangered or threatened.
- Do you know of any threatened or endangered species in Canada?
- What is the difference between an endangered species and a species that is threatened?
- List some species that have become extinct within the past thousand years.
- List factors that adversely affect animal species.
- What conservation or environmental organizations that work to protect endangered species have you heard about?

GETTING STARTED

Two mathematical models will be investigated in this project. The first considers growth in a population of an endangered species raised in captivity, in a protected environment such as a zoo or small wildlife sanctuary. The population begins from a small number of breeding pairs. The second model considers a larger population that lives in the wild. This type of model considers varying growth rates and assumes that there is a maximum sustainable population for a given habitat area. In this Getting Started section, you will consider the whooping crane.

1. The whooping crane can live 25 years. Birds reach sexual maturity at age 4 years and lay 2 eggs every year thereafter. In the wild, one of the chicks usually kills the other. In a breeding program, both chicks may survive. Table 1 tracks the number of whooping cranes in a captive breeding program started with 3 breeding pairs (6 birds). Fill in the table for the first 15 years. Assume all the chicks survive and mate at sexual maturity.

2. Use the data in Table 1 to graph the population of whooping cranes as a function of the number of years for up to 15 years.

Table 1 Non-Release Captive Breeding Program

Year	Number of Breeding Birds	Whooping Cranes Aged 3 Years	Whooping Cranes Aged 2 Years	Whooping Cranes Aged 1 Year	Newborn Whooping Cranes	Total Population in Captivity
1	6	0	0	0	6	12
2	6	0	0	6	6	18
3	6	0	6	6	6	24
4						
5						
6						
7						
8						
9						
10						
11						
12						
13						
14						
15						

3. a) The Fibonacci sequence is the well-known sequence 1, 1, 2, 3, 5, 8, 13, …. Observe that a given term (from the third term onward) in the Fibonacci sequence may be obtained by adding the two preceding terms. State the next three terms in the Fibonacci sequence.

b) The first four terms in a sequence are: 12, 18, 24, and 30. The 5th term is defined as the sum of the 4th term and the 1st term. That is, $\text{term}_5 = 30 + 12 = 42$. Additional terms are defined in the same manner.

$$\text{Term}_6 = \text{Term}_5 + \text{Term}_2 = 60$$

How is this sequence related to the data in Table 1?

4. a) Set up a spreadsheet to produce Table 1. Use the spreadsheet to determine the population of birds for up to 25 years. Why must the spreadsheet be adjusted after this time?

b) Adjust the spreadsheet so that the assumption that both chicks survive is changed to only one chick survives.

c) Consider the sequence that shows the total population of cranes, given the assumption that only one chick survives. How could you define a term in this sequence?

d) List the first 15 terms of this sequence and graph the sequence on the same axes as exercise 2. Label this graph.

Animals in the wild require a minimum habitat area to survive. If a habitat area is reduced due to human activities such as logging, mining, and damming for hydro-electric power, fewer animals will be able to survive in the area and the population will decline. The following exercises develop a theoretical model. This model incorporates the concept of a maximum sustainable population for a given animal species within a given area.

5. Consider a species in the wild with a habitat area that can support a maximum population, M, of 100 individuals. Consider a population with a maximum growth rate, r, of 25% *when food and space are unrestricted*. The model, produced by Pierre Verhulst (1804–1849), assumes that each year's growth rate depends upon the previous year's population size. This model, therefore, has a *variable growth rate*. The growth rate is assumed to vary *linearly* as shown in the graph below.

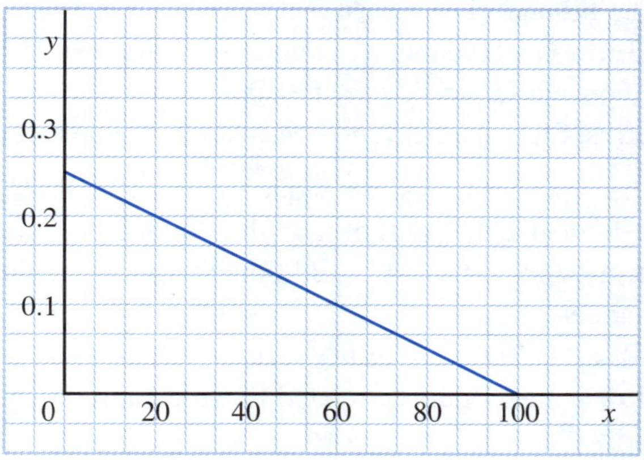

If the variables x and y are changed to p and R respectively, to reflect the fact that the x-axis represents population and the y-axis the variable rate, then the growth rate can be expressed by the equation

$$R = r\left(1 - \frac{p}{M}\right).$$

a) Generate values for R using a spreadsheet, or alternatively, read values off the graph.

b) A sequence that models the growth of a population with a variable growth rate R, can now be developed by considering the equation Next year's population = Previous year's population + R (previous year's population).
It is necessary to know the size of the population at the time the study commences. Consider a small flock of whooping cranes in the wild with an initial population of 40, an unrestricted growth rate, r, of 25%, and the maximum sustainable population, M, for the area of 100 individuals. List the first 20 terms of the sequence. Use a calculator or set up a spreadsheet to calculate each term of the sequence.

c) Graph the sequence from part b for up to 20 years. What happens to the growth rate of the cranes over this period?

d) Consider an initial population of 200 birds in the same study area. This exceeds the maximum sustainable limit for the habitat. List the first 20 terms of the sequence and graph the sequence.

Threatened and Endangered

species

PROJECT PRESENTATION

Use what you have learned in Getting Started to develop your project. You will research an endangered species. If you wish, you may continue to study the whooping crane and include the work done in the Getting Started exercises.

Your completed project will consist of the following.

- An information pamphlet or web site on the endangered species of your choice
- Graphs to show theoretical population increases for a variety of breeding programs in captivity
- A graph to illustrate the theoretical decline in population in the wild when there is not enough habitat space available

Here is a detailed description of your responsibilities. Share the tasks equally.

Wildlife Biologists (2): For your chosen species, obtain the following information:

- current population
- life span
- time to reach sexual maturity
- fertility rate
- habitat requirements
- major food requirements
- risk factors that make this species endangered
- any programs that are designed to help the species

Include graphs to illustrate that the theoretical population increases for non-release captive breeding programs. Use the data on the time required to reach sexual maturity and the fertility rate (obtained from mating frequency and number of surviving infants per mating) to generate the population estimates for these graphs.

Include another graph or graphs to track the population results for a breeding program in which animals are released into the wild on a regular basis. Decide on how many animals are to be released into the wild and how often release will occur.

Prepare a graph that illustrates the theoretical decline of a population of animals when numbers exceed the maximum sustainable limit for a particular area. Feature other relevant information from your research.

Career Opportunities

Wildlife biologists carry out in-depth studies that involve observation, sampling, record keeping, and research skills. An understanding of the mathematics of population dynamics and the nature of sequences is required. In addition to conservation activities and breeding programs, wildlife biologists act as expert witnesses for the environmental impact studies necessary before major development projects are commenced.

Building the Best Soft-Drink Container

Suggested Group Size: 3

Materials: A 355-mL soft-drink can, a computer with spreadsheet software, materials to create a poster

THE TASK

In this project, you will design a soft-drink container for optimum size and cost. Your group will include a project manager, a data processing technician, and a marketing expert.

BACKGROUND

As a recent employee of Kula Kola Company, you have been waiting for an opportunity to demonstrate your abilities. Several teams have been selected to design a new cylindrical soft-drink container for the various soft drinks produced by the company. The container must hold the standard 355-mL volume of soft drink. The design should have maximum appeal for consumers but involve minimum materials and costs. You are expected to present a convincing argument to the company's executives in support of your design.

Consider a cylinder. Visualize how a change in the height of the cylinder will affect its shape, if the volume is kept constant at 355 mL.

A short, wide design

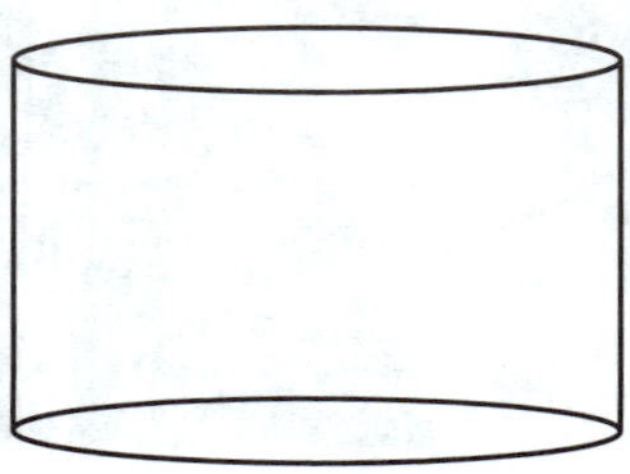

A tall, narrow design

Designs not to scale

SOURCE LINK

- To review sequences, refer to the Source Book, Chapter 6: Patterns. If you need to review volume and surface area, refer to the Source Book, Student Reference.

Kula-Kola

Building the Best Soft-Drink Container

- What is the surface area of the different designs you can create?
- How does the surface area affect the production cost of the can?
- Does the current design of a soft-drink container have any benefits?
- What would be the advantages of a container of a different shape?

GETTING STARTED

Consider what shapes are possible for soft-drink containers that hold 355 mL of liquid. Analyze the production cost of the different containers.

1. Investigate how the volume and surface area of a can change as its radius and height change. Ignore the restriction that the can must hold 355 mL of liquid.

Volume: $V = \pi r^2 h$

Surface area: $A = 2\pi r^2 + 2\pi rh$

a) Create a spreadsheet to calculate the volume and surface area of a cylindrical can that has radius 10 cm and height 20 cm. In each successive row of the spreadsheet, halve the previous radius and height.

b) Predict the surface area and volume of the 6th can in this progression.

c) Write an expression for the surface area after you carry out the procedure n times.

d) Write an expression for the volume after you carry out the procedure n times.

2. Consider that all the containers must hold 355 mL of liquid. This means you will work with the following two formulas.

Volume: $355 = \pi r^2 h$ ①

Surface Area: $A = 2\pi r^2 + 2\pi rh$ ②

a) Solve formula ① for h.

b) Substitute the expression for h into formula ②.

c) Create a spreadsheet to calculate the height and surface area for cans of radius from 1 to 10 cm.

Radius (cm)	Height (cm)	Surface Area (cm^2)
1.0		
2.0		
3.0		

d) Add a column to the spreadsheet to calculate the production costs for the different cans. The cost of aluminum is \$0.0005/cm^2.

3. Examine your results from exercise 2.

a) What radius and height for the soft-drink container result in the lowest production costs?

b) How do these measurements compare to those of aluminum soft-drink cans currently in use?

Building the Best Soft-Drink Container

PROJECT PRESENTATION

Use what you learned in Getting Started to begin your project. Your completed project will include the following:

- An evaluation of the factors, other than cost, involved in the determination of can shape (could include acceptability to consumers, costs of promotion campaigns to change consumer attitude, and aspects of storage)
- A copy of all spreadsheets created and all calculations used
- A life-size model of the new can design
- A written explanation as to why this design should be chosen
- A poster that incorporates all the above information in a form suitable for a marketing campaign

Here are detailed descriptions of each person's responsibilities.

Project Manager: You are responsible for the organization of the project. Collect all the materials needed, monitor the data, and work with the Data Processing Technician to design the spreadsheets. Once the data analysis is complete, lead the discussion of the factors involved in the final design. Ensure that the Marketing Expert has all the materials necessary to create the promotional poster, and assist in the construction of the life-size model of the new soft-drink container.

Data Processing Technician: You will create all the spreadsheets used to analyze the different sizes of soft-drink container. Consult with your team members to ensure your formulas are correct. Once you have compiled the data, give them to the Marketing Expert for use in the promotional poster. You are also responsible for completing any other calculations necessary for the analysis of the new design.

Marketing Expert: Once the group has determined the design of the new container, you will build the life-size model. Check the calculations that the Data Processing Technician completes. You will present these results, so you need to ensure they are correct. Assemble all the materials and analysis in a poster to promote the new design.

Career Opportunities

The soft-drink industry employs many kinds of managers, and data analysis and marketing experts. Competition is fierce and new ways to promote and encourage sales of the company's soft-drink products are sought continually. Initiative and creativity are greatly rewarded.

Flight Simulator DEVELOPMENT

THE TASK

In this project, you will use vector analysis to develop and solve flight simulator scenarios.

Suggested Group Size: 2

Materials: Grid paper; Internet access (optional)

BACKGROUND

Aircraft pilots can hone their skills on computer-generated flight simulators. These simulators allow them to experience the effects of wind and speed on the handling of an aircraft, while doing so in complete safety.

Flight simulators can be programmed to recreate weather conditions, such as wind sheer or downdrafts, so that pilots can test their skills under a variety of flight conditions. Simulators that create the environments of major airports give commercial pilots opportunities to practise landing at these locations.

- What are two advantages of flight simulators?
- Why might simulators be used to train pilots?
- Why might the use of a simulator be beneficial for an experienced pilot?
- What are some disadvantages to using a flight simulator?

SOURCE LINK

- To review vector analysis, refer to the Source Book, Chapter 7: Vectors.

Flight Simulator
DEVELOPMENT

GETTING STARTED

Each of the following exercises represents a scenario that could be programmed into a flight simulator.

1. A plane cruises at an airspeed of 200 km/h. It encounters an opposing head wind gust of 50 km/h. Draw a scale diagram to show vector addition of these velocities. Use the drawing to find the magnitude and direction of the resultant velocity of the plane.

2. A Boeing 747SP cruises at 650 km/h and encounters a tail wind of 50 km/h. Draw a scale diagram to show vector addition of these velocities. Use the drawing to find the magnitude and direction of the resultant velocity of the plane.

3. A plane travels north at 400 km/h and encounters a wind moving at 50 km/h toward the west. Draw a scale diagram to show vector addition of these velocities. Use the drawing to find the magnitude and direction of the resultant velocity of the plane.

4. An aircraft that heads west at 600 km/h encounters a wind blowing at 50 km/h toward the north. Draw a scale diagram to show vector addition of these velocities. Use the drawing to find the magnitude and direction of the resultant velocity of the plane.

5. A plane that travels at 450 km/h encounters a downdraft of 100 km/h. Find the angle and speed of descent if the pilot takes no opposing action. Draw a scale diagram to show vector addition of these velocities. Use the drawing to find the magnitude and direction of the resultant velocity of the plane.

6. A glider travels at 50 km/h and attempts to climb at a pitch of 10° above the horizontal. It enters a downdraft of air at an angle of 20° below the horizontal and a speed of 30 km/h in the same direction that the glider is travelling. Draw a scale diagram to show vector addition of these velocities. Use the drawing to find the magnitude and direction of the resultant velocity of the glider.

PROJECT PRESENTATION

Use what you learned in Getting Started to begin your project. You are to create a number of scenarios to be programmed into a flight simulator for the training program on a Challenger 604 jet aircraft. Research specific conditions appropriate to this aircraft at the library or on the Internet.

You must deal with wind effects such as tail wind, head wind, downdraft, updraft, and winds coming from a variety of compass directions.

Your completed project will include the following:

- 5 scenarios for flight simulation
- A scale vector diagram to represent each scenario and its resultant vector
- A brief description of how each scenario might arise during flight

Here is a description of your responsibilities.

Flight Simulation Programmers (2): Each of you must create 5 scenarios and provide solutions that use vector representations. At least 1 of the 5 scenarios must include a wind with vertical and horizontal components. A 3-dimensional representation of the effects of this wind on the plane should be included. Assume all circumstances begin with the plane travelling due North (0°) at cruising altitude and at an airspeed of 500 km/h. To lend some realism to the simulations, each programmer should research the weather conditions that might give rise to the circumstances described in the scenarios. Thunderstorms and wind sheer might be good starting places for research.

Once each programmer has created and solved 5 scenarios, exchange the scenarios and check the clarity of the questions and the correctness of the solutions. Choose 5 of the scenarios to include in your presentation. Include at least one 3-dimensional representation.

Career Opportunities

There is an increasing demand for computer programmers and game/simulator designers. Graphic design requires design and computer skills and is another field that provides many opportunities for employment.

TRACKING POLLUTION

Suggested Group Size: 2

Materials: Grid paper; Internet access (optional)

THE TASK

In this project, you will examine the possibility that radioactive wastes travel via ocean currents and investigate possible effects of radioactive wastes on living things. You will use vector analysis to track the movement of pollutants in a model case.

BACKGROUND

Over the years, the world's oceans, rivers, and lakes have been used as chemical dumps. Water pollution in the form of mercury poisoning caused horrific birth defects in Japan. Drums of radioactive wastes have been dumped into the oceans from ships. Buried wastes have leached from containers into waterways and supplies of drinking water. Contamination of water supplies by a virulent form of *E. coli* has been linked to deaths in Ontario. All these situations are cause for concern; pollution control agreements and careful monitoring are needed to avoid similar problems.

Because natural bodies of water are dynamic moving masses, chemical pollutants can travel from their place of origin to places where their damage can be profound. Oceanographers and marine biologists are often called on to trace the origins of pollutants in an attempt to reduce or prevent damage to people and the environment in general.

In this project, you will study environments in which water moves as the result of currents or river flow. You will use vector analysis to predict the path of materials placed in such environments.

SOURCE LINK

- To review vector analysis, refer to the Source Book, Chapter 7: Vectors. For help with exponential equations and radioactive decay, see the Student Reference.

Oil spill clean-up

TRACKING

POLLUTION

- What are some of the pollutants found in water?
- How do they get there?
- What are some ways that water pollution travels?
- What are some sources of radioactive waste?
- What does the term *half-life* mean?

GETTING STARTED

1. Suppose a ship that carries toxic chemicals sinks in an area where the ocean depth is 500 m. If the ship descended at an angle of 60º from the horizontal and its velocity was 6 km/h in that same direction, how many minutes would it take to reach the ocean bottom? How far would the ship have travelled in a horizontal direction during the time it was sinking?

2. The current in a river 100-m wide is 2 m/s. A chemical is discharged across the river at point A with a dispersal rate of 0.5 m/s. How far down the river from point A would the chemical first appear on the opposite shore? Draw and label a vector diagram that shows the solution to this problem.

3. Consider the illustration of Halifax Harbour.

a) If 0 is midnight, what time of the day does the illustration represent?

b) What is the mathematical term that best describes the shape of the elevation/time function?

c) The small arrows are current vectors. What two scalar quantities does each arrow tell you?

d) Where is the scale of the current vectors shown?

e) Why are the current vectors longest in the narrow part of the channel?

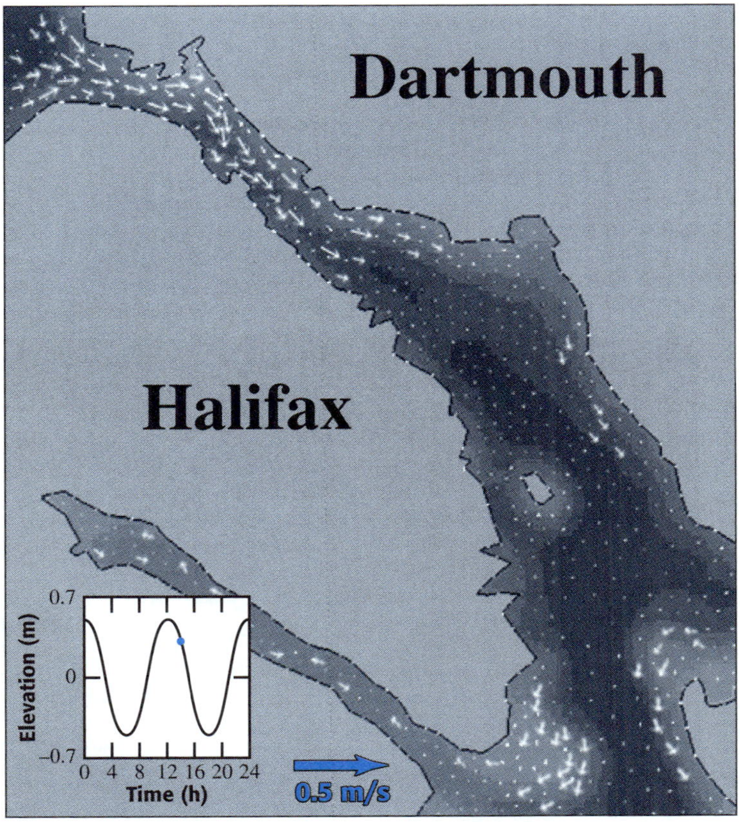

Photo courtesy of Fisheries and Oceans, Maritimes Region.

Adapted from www.mar.dfo-mpo.gc.ca/science/ocean/coastal_hydrodynamics/table_5/2c.html

4. Iodine-131 has a half-life of 8 d. Cobalt-60 has a half-life of 5.27 years.

a) Estimate how long it takes for a sample of iodine-131 to decay to 10% of its original mass.

b) Estimate how long it takes for a sample of cobalt-60 to decay to 10% of its original mass.

TRACKING POLLUTION

PROJECT PRESENTATION

Use what you learned in Getting Started to begin your project. Model the possible results of a dump of radioactive waste on the west coast of North America. The location of the dump is shown on the map below.

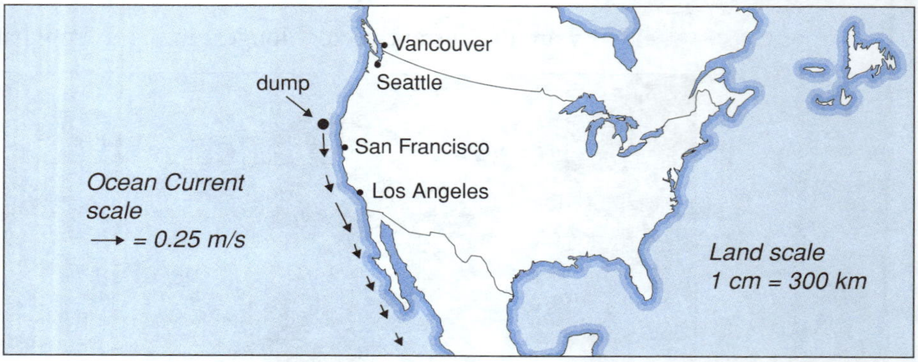

Your completed project will include the following items:

- An appropriately scaled map of the study area
- A vector analysis of the movement of the pollutants over a period of 3 months
- A list of types of life form in areas likely to be affected
- A discussion of potential effects of radioactivity on these life forms

Here are detailed descriptions of each person's responsibilities.

Oceanographer: Copy the map of the study area, scaled appropriately to fit an 8.5 by 11-inch piece of grid paper. Clearly label the features found in the original map. Note that a cold current runs south-east, approximately parallel to the coast of California. If radioactive wastes were dumped at the point indicated, show on your map how the currents would move the wastes and where one would expect to find radioactive materials after a period of 3 months. Suggest possible types of radioactive waste that might have been released in the study area and discuss the radioactive substances involved.

Marine Biologist: Study the map and determine the types of life forms likely to be affected by the radioactivity in the wastes. Research the effects of radioactivity on living things. Write a report on the possible effects of radioactive pollutants in the study area; specifically, discuss radioactive half-lives, cancer, and mutations.

Career Opportunities

Oceanographers and their technical assistants have a love of the ocean. They need a good background in ocean studies and an understanding of the mathematics of the forces that affect the oceans. Economic planners and those involved in the nuclear industry need to understand the long-term challenges involved in disposal of radioactive wastes.

Training a ROBOT

THE TASK

In this project, you will explore the use of vectors to guide robots. You will measure distances and directions, and plan routes to minimize command programming and travel distances. You will use vectors and multiply them by scalars, determine resultants, model vector solutions, and use the fundamental counting principle.

Suggested Group Size: 2

Materials: Training a Robot Templates A, B, and C, grid paper, ruler, protractor, tape measure; access to geometry software such as *The Geometer's Sketchpad*, *Sketchpad* diagrams Robot Plate A & B, available on *CD-ROM*, Internet access (optional)

SOURCE LINK

- For a review of vectors, refer to the Source Book, Chapter 7: Vectors. For the fundamental counting principle, see the Source Book, Chapter 1: Probability.

BACKGROUND

Robotics is used extensively in industry, especially in assembly processes. A robotic welder can spot-weld the body of a car in dozens of places to within fractions of a millimetre. Robots are also used in some large offices to deliver mail. Robots are especially effective in roles where a series of movements and actions are repeated over and over. A system is needed to direct the robot through these actions; vectors can be used.

We use vectors often when we give directions.

- How would you describe the best route from the school's main entrance to the door of your classroom?
- What are some ways to describe or define distances?
- Is there some natural reference system you use for direction?
- Research direction system conventions used around the world.
- Why is it important to have consistent direction conventions?

Training a ROBOT

GETTING STARTED

1. What is the shortest pathway from your place in your classroom to the opposite wall in the hall outside the main door of your classroom? Can you go there in one straight line? (Do not jump over desks or other obstacles!) How many lines or paths does it take? Draw a diagram to show the paths you would need to take. Estimate distances and use a scale for your personal exit diagram.

2. How would you describe the directions of your paths to get out of the classroom? Is there a natural direction system? Devise a consistent convention for measuring directions in your school. Share this convention with other groups. How many different systems were devised? Come to a consensus within the class on a school direction system. Apply this direction convention to your exit diagram from exercise 1.

3. Compare your exit diagram to those of others near you in the class. The diagrams should be almost the same if your direction convention is consistent and you allow for scale differences. Compare your diagram to that of someone on the far side of the class. The diagrams should be different. What part of the exit diagram is different for people on opposite sides of the classroom? What part should be the same?

Each pathway drawn is a displacement vector that involves both magnitude (distance) and direction. A robot could follow vector directions to take pathways from one location to another. Some more sophisticated robots have interactive sensors that allow them to avoid obstacles and reprogram themselves by reorienting coordinates.

4. Obtain copies of Training a Robot: Templates A, B, and C from your teacher, or, if you use *The Geometer's Sketchpad*, open the sketch Robot Plate A & B. Note the scales and direction conventions on the templates. The robot cannot pass through the shaded areas. On Template A, begin at Start. Draw a series of straight lines to indicate a route your robot could follow to visit all three labelled points F, N, and J, and return to Start. Label each line as a vector and include the distance and the direction. How many different vectors are needed? Could you use more vectors? Are all routes the same? What is the minimum total route? How would your vectors be different if your robot followed the route backward? How many ways are there to visit the points?

5. On Training a Robot: Template B, you are given a start position and a set of vector directions. Use the same scale and direction convention as for Template A. Draw the vectors listed below to create a route for your robot.

- 4 m at [180°]
- 8.5 m at [300°]
- 2 m at [0°]
- 6.5 m at [150°]
- 2.5 m at [250°]

Where does the robot end up? What is the resultant vector and why can it not be used as a single command for the robot? Can you think of some situations where it is important to know the shortest path between 2 points? Could you change the order of the vectors and still end up at the same point? What vectors would you choose to have the robot end at point C? Which point(s) can you reach with 1 vector? Can you reach all other points with 2 vectors?

6. Training a Robot: Template C is a partial floor plan of a building. The robot does regular security checks by following vector commands. Take the robot from Start to visit all security points. The robot must be centred on a security point to make a successful check. Compile a list of vector commands for the robot. Use as few defined vectors as possible. You may reuse a defined vector any number of times. Shorten your command list by the use of scalar multiplication of vectors.

PROJECT PRESENTATION

With your teacher's guidance, choose a reference point in your classroom or hallway. From this reference point, determine the location of four landmarks around your school. Examples of landmarks are: a water fountain, the main office doorway, or the 1998 Grad class photo. Use what you learned in Getting Started to create a map and a set of vector diagrams to direct a robot along a route to visit your landmarks. Follow another group's vector diagrams to the landmarks along their route.

Your completed project will include the following:

- Templates A, B, and C with vector diagrams and command lists completed
- A discussion of various direction systems

Training a ROBOT

- A clear grid map (with scale, direction convention, and any obstacles indicated) of your school landmarks in relation to your reference point
- A set of vector commands to direct a robot along a route to visit your landmarks
- A notation of the shortest resultant vector between each set of points on your route
- A report on your attempt to follow another group's vector commands along a route to a different set of landmarks
- A plot of this route on your map
- A discussion (with more examples) of ideas for vector directions for training a robot

Here is a description of your responsibilities.

Robot Trainers (2): Work together to measure distances and directions to your landmarks. Create your set of vector directions for the robot and determine the shortest resultant vector between each set of points on the route. Test the efficiency of another group's vector directions.

Career Opportunities

Vectors are useful in many areas. Winch operators need to know how force vectors combine to get the job done. Pilots use velocity and displacement vectors in navigation. Computer graphics programmers and game developers can use vectors to define the motion of objects.

Training a Robot: Template A

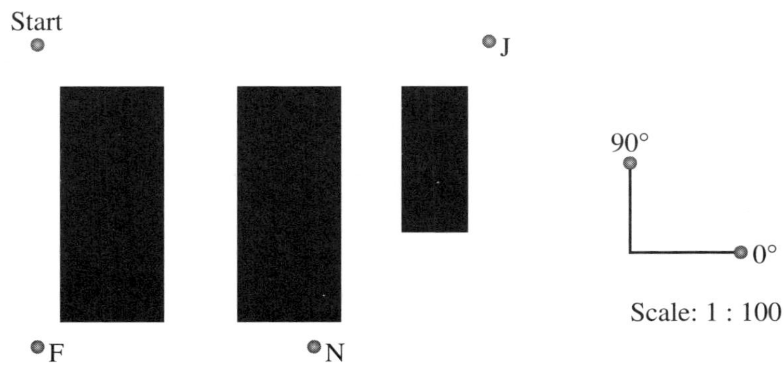

Training a Robot: Template B

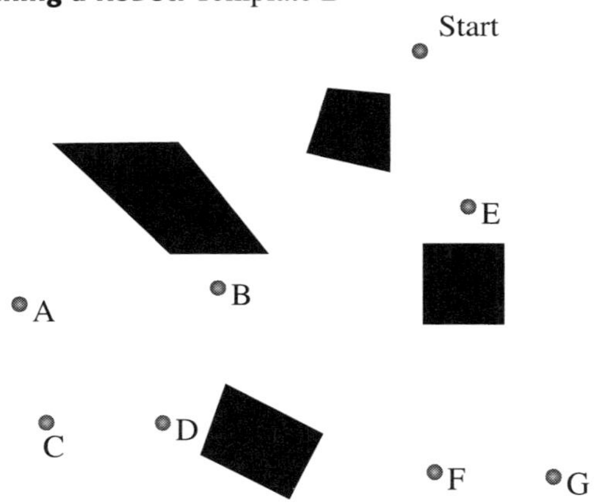

Training a Robot: Template C

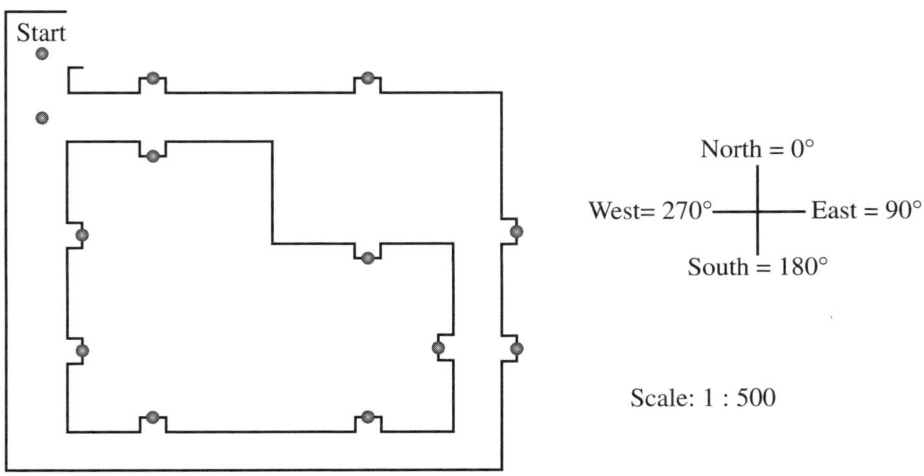

Shelving SYSTEMS

THE TASK

In this project, you will design, cost, package, and market a home-assembly shelving system for a clothes closet. You will work with dimensions, unit prices, budgets, and spreadsheets.

Suggested Group Size: 2

Materials: Newspapers, flyers, or magazines that advertise closet organizers, grid paper; a computer with a spreadsheet program (optional)

BACKGROUND

Many furniture stores sell inexpensive kits that the customer assembles at home. These kits contain a set of instructions, pre-cut parts, and all the nuts, bolts, and screws required. They are inexpensive because the components can be mass produced and packaged in units, and there are no labour costs for assembly. Shelving systems for clothes closets are suitable for such kits. Clothes closet systems can be made to fit inside an already existing closet or to stand independently. Shelving systems are often made so that customers can adjust the height of the shelves to suit their own needs.

- What size shelves or compartments are needed for clothes closets?
- What would be a suitable height for a hanging section of a clothes closet?
- How might you store shoes efficiently?
- What materials might be suitable to construct clothes closets?
- What colours might be suitable for clothes closets?
- What are the approximate dimensions of your own and your friends' clothes closets?
- Visit a furniture store, consult advertisements, or look at furniture at home or at a friend's house to see styles and methods of assembly.

SOURCE LINK

- To review the use of spreadsheets in financial transactions, refer to the Source Book, Chapter 4: Personal Finance. For help with formatting spreadsheets, see Utility 31. To review area and volume see the Student Reference

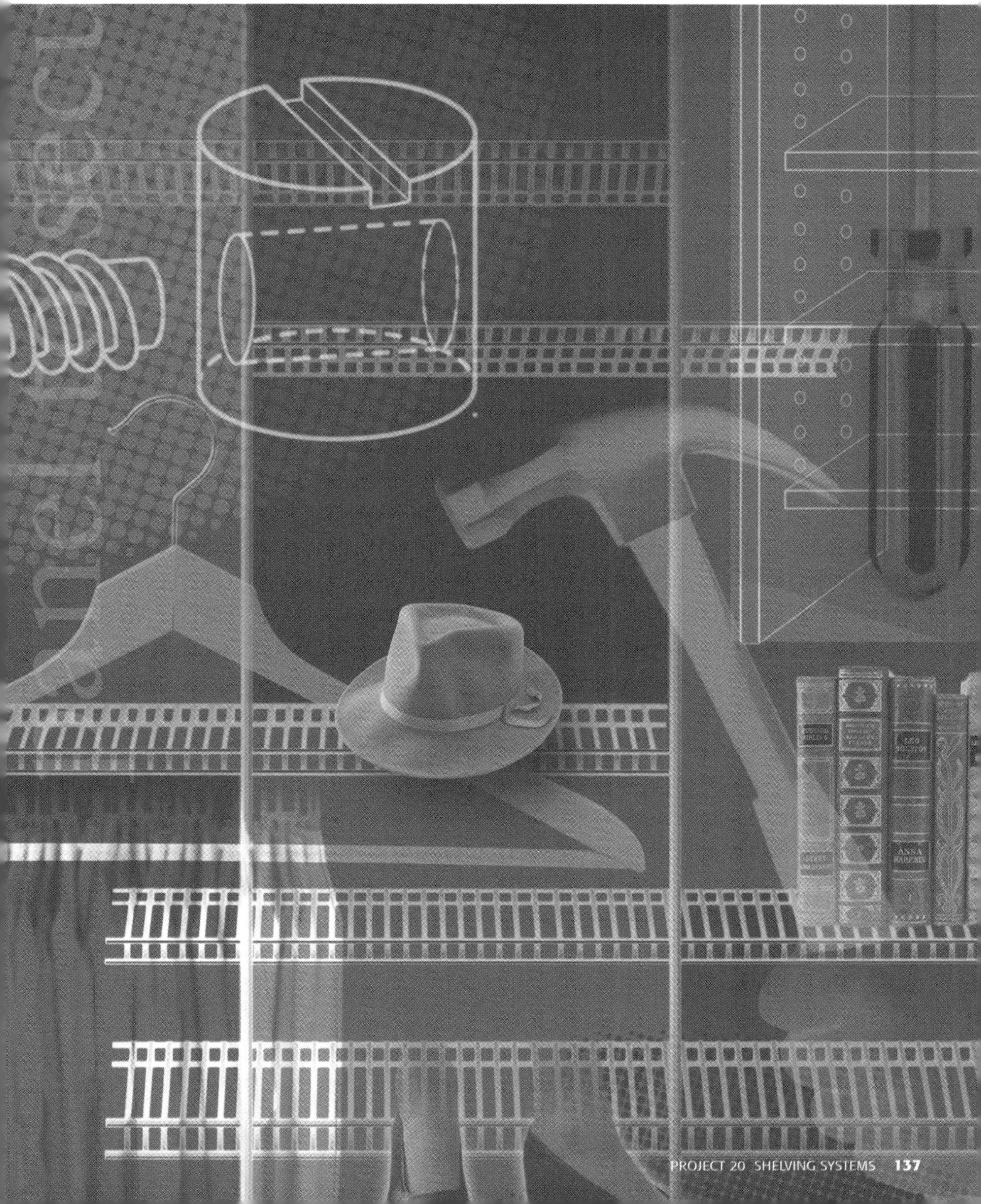

Shelving SYSTEMS

GETTING STARTED

Examine the shelf unit below.

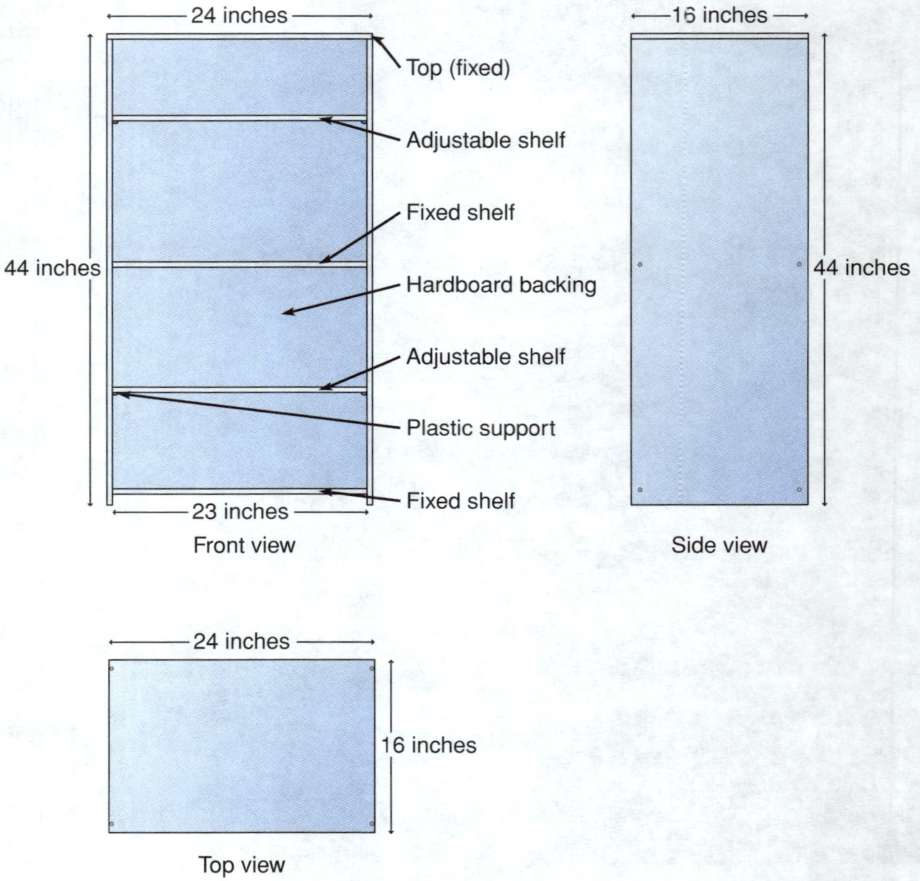

1. The shelves, sides, and top are made from $\frac{1}{2}$-inch thick melamine (laminated particle board) that may be purchased in sheets. All visible edges of the shelving unit must be laminated. The sheets come in two sizes, 48 inch by 96 inch, which costs \$20 per sheet, and 16 inch by 96 inch, which costs \$8 per sheet. All edges of the 48-inch by 96-inch sheet are unlaminated. The 16-inch by 96-inch sheet has its two long edges already laminated. Laminated edging costs \$0.15 for 12 inches. Work out possible layouts for the sides, top, and shelves of the unit above. Which of your layouts has the lowest price?

2. The backing for the shelves is cut from a thin sheet of hardboard. The hardboard costs \$7 for a 4-foot by 8-foot (48-inch by 96-inch) sheet. How many backs can be cut from one sheet? The backing is attached using 20 $\frac{1}{4}$-inch finishing nails that cost a total of \$0.10. The sides and top fit together with 12 nuts and bolts that cost \$0.50 each pair. The diagram below shows how they fasten together.

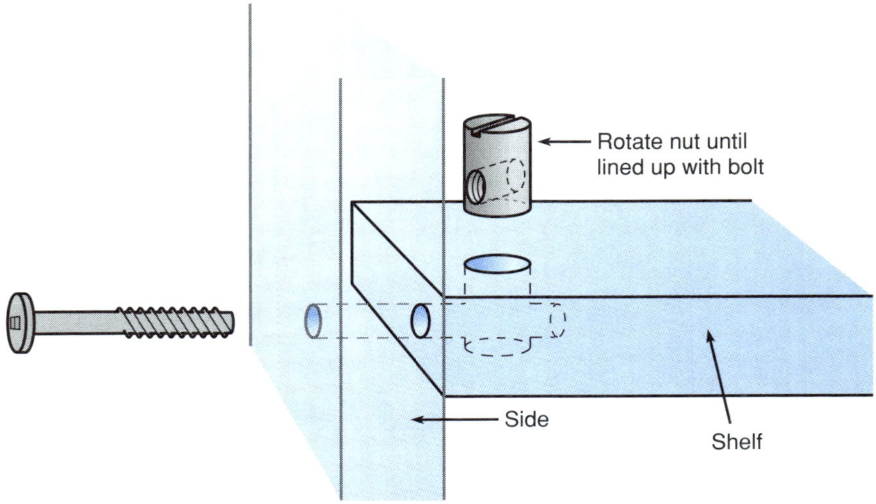

3. The shelves have plastic supports to allow the heights of two of the shelves to be adjusted. Examine the diagram below. The plastic shelf support is cylindrical with a flat section. What is its volume?

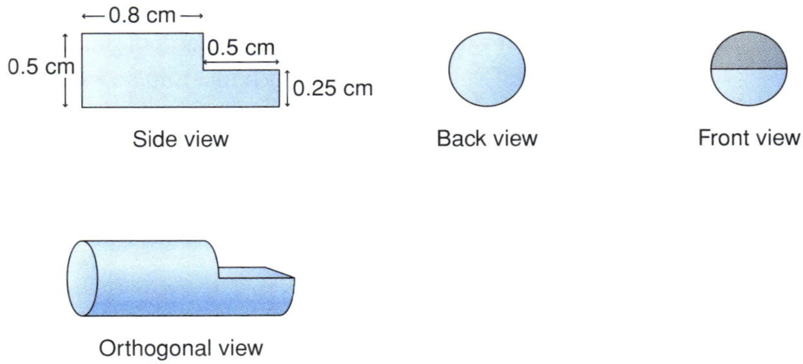

4. The plastic shelf supports are made in an injection mould. The plastic costs 0.5¢/cm^3. What is the materials cost to produce 10 supports?

Shelving SYSTEMS

5. A list of the component parts of this shelf unit is given below. Devise a clear set of instructions for its assembly.

   Parts List: 2 sides, 1 top, 2 fixed shelves, 2 adjustable shelves, 1 back, 10 nuts, 12 bolts, 8 plastic shelf supports, 20 finishing nails

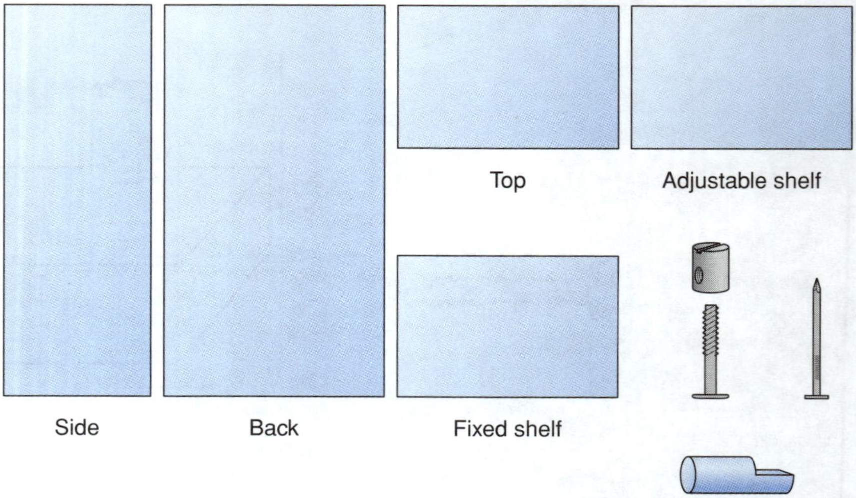

6. Determine the dimensions of a cardboard box in which to package this shelf unit. Cardboard packaging can be purchased for \$0.05 per square foot. What does the box cost? A plastic bag is needed to contain the small parts, shelf supports, finishing nails, and so on. How much does this bag cost?

7. Produce a spreadsheet template that itemizes the parts for this shelving unit and shows a breakdown of all costs, including packaging.

PROJECT PRESENTATION

Use what you learned in Getting Started to develop your detailed plans for a clothes closet system.

Your completed project will include the following:

- Assembly instructions
- A list of parts and the number of each part required
- The dimensions of the cardboard box and plastic bag used for packaging
- The cost breakdown for the materials, including packaging, calculated on a spreadsheet
- An illustration of the completed system suitable for a catalogue
- A scale model of the system (optional)

Here are detailed descriptions of each person's responsibilities.

Furniture Designer: Design a clothes closet system suitable for young adults. Show accurate scale diagrams of a front view, side view, and top view, and include all appropriate dimensions. Include a description of how the adjustable shelves work. Supply diagrams with dimensions of all pieces of hardware (such as nuts, bolts, finishing nails, and plastic shelf supports). Include a list of parts and quantities needed, and a picture of each item. Give clear and concise assembly instructions, including diagrams.

Marketing and Packaging Manager: Determine the dimensions of the cardboard box used for packaging. Determine the costs of all materials, including packaging. Use a spreadsheet program to detail the cost for each item, the quantity of each item, and the total cost. Sketch a picture of the completed closet for use in a catalogue. Build a cardboard scale model of your system, if you wish.

Career Opportunities

Skills in design and technical drawing have applications to many industries. Detail-oriented individuals with planning and computer skills find employment as product managers, inventory controllers, and in sales and marketing.

TOY DESIGN

Suggested Group Size: 3

Materials: Ruler, grid paper, examples of plastic toys of various shapes and dimensions; Internet access (optional)

THE TASK

In this project, you will solve problems related to design and cost in the manufacture of plastic toys.

BACKGROUND

The market for plastic toys is very large. Plastic is colourful, cheap, durable, and easily injected into moulds. In any manufacturing operation it is essential that the cost of production be known. Precise knowledge of costs allows the manufacturer to set a realistic price for the product.

- Where do you think most plastic toys are manufactured? Why?
- What types of plastic toys break easily? Why?
- What is an injection mould? How does it work?
- What factors influence the cost of manufacturing plastic toys?

SOURCE LINK

- If you need to review matrices, refer to the Source Book, Chapter 2: Matrices. For help with matrix operations on the TI-83, see Utility 26. For a review of volume and surface area, refer to the Student Reference.

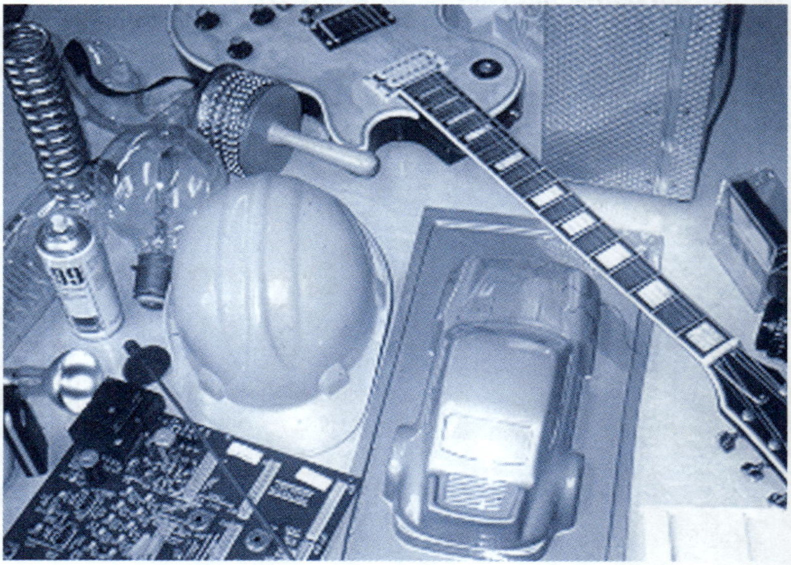

TOY DESIGN

GETTING STARTED

1. Review the formulas for volume and surface area of the following shapes: cube, sphere, cylinder, cone, and rectangular prism. Sketch each into your notes and record the appropriate formulas.

2. Determine the volume and surface area of the following 3-dimensional solids.

a) a cube of side 2 cm

b) a rectangular prism 8 cm by 8 cm by 4 cm

c) a sphere of radius 2 cm

d) a cylinder of radius 2 cm and height 8 cm

e) a cylinder of radius 1 cm and height 8 cm

f) a cone of radius 2 cm and height 8 cm

3. Large plastic shapes are often designed as toys for small children, whose small motor skills are still developing. Assume plastic costs $0.1¢/cm^3$. Determine the cost of the material to produce each of the objects in exercise 2, if the volume of each object is to be occupied by plastic. Compare the cost of the plastic objects to that of painted wooden objects, where wood costs $0.2¢/cm^3$ and paint costs $0.1¢/cm^2$.

4. Assume each shape described in exercise 2 is to be packed in a cardboard box that is a cube or a rectangular prism. Determine the dimensions of the minimum-size box needed to fit each object.

5. Many excellent toys are made of pieces that can be joined together. For the moment, ignore the connecting links that would be required to enable pieces to snap together. Find the cost of the plastic required to build the toy shown below, using the basic pieces described in exercise 2.

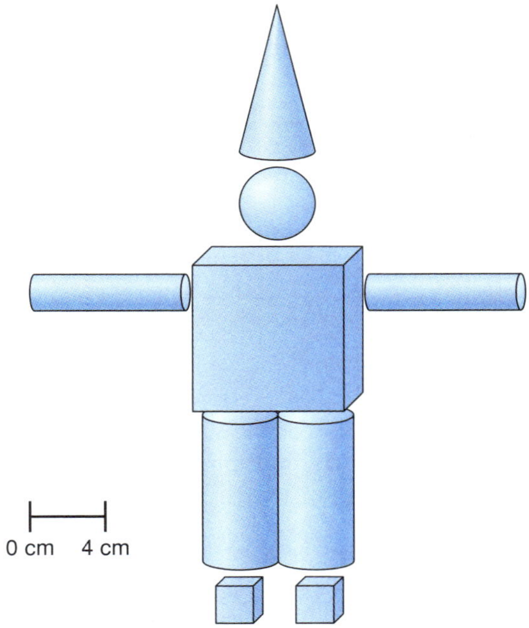

6. If the pieces required for the toy in exercise 5 were sold as a set, what is the minimum size of box needed to fit all 9 pieces?

7. How many 9-piece kits could be made if the budget for plastic were $200?

8. Table 1 shows the contents of 3 kits of plastic shapes.

Table 1

Kit #	Cube	Prism	Sphere	Cylinder 1	Cylinder 2	Cone
1 Introductory	2	1	1	2	2	1
2 Standard	6	3	2	4	4	2
3 DeLuxe	8	4	3	8	8	3

Create a 3 by 6 Kit–Shape matrix from this table.

TOY DESIGN

Table 2 shows the cost of the plastic needed for each object. Record your results from exercise 3 to complete the table. Create a 6 by 1 Shape–Cost matrix from the table.

Table 2

Shape	Cost
Cube	
Prism	
Sphere	
Cylinder 1	
Cylinder 2	
Cone	

Use matrix multiplication to obtain the cost for each kit. Record your results in a table.

PROJECT PRESENTATION

You will create toy construction kits from the basic geometric figures used in Getting Started. You will decide the number of each shape to put in a kit, the size of the pieces, and the dimensions of the packaging. Give examples of toys that could be made if the pieces were interlocking.

Assume you work for a toy manufacturing company and you have been asked to produce a toy kit with the following parameters:

- Objects are smaller than those in Getting Started; for example, a rectangular prism 4 cm by 4 cm by 2 cm.
- It contains at least 1 of each shape.
- It contains at least 30 pieces.

Your completed project should include the following:

- The contents of a kit of at least 30 pieces, listing size, number, and colour of the pieces and reasons why this kit was chosen
- Tables and matrices, or spreadsheets, to show a cost breakdown for the manufacture of components in the kit

- The dimensions of a box just large enough to contain the kit, or suggestions for alternative packaging
- Designs for 3 toys that could be made from the kit, with instructions on how to modify the pieces to snap together to form the toys
- An advertising brochure that includes a name and logo for the kit and pictorial diagrams of each of the selected toys

Here is a description of your responsibilities.

Designers (3): Each member of the design team will create 3 toys that use the basic shapes, suggest the composition of 3 kits, and cost the plastic required for each kit. The team will choose from among the 9 kits to create the best kit with regard to the number of toys possible and the cost of materials. The team will operate within a materials budget of $200. The kit chosen will include at least one toy idea from each member of the team.

Career Opportunities

Toy design needs people who can adapt skills in design and use of colour to many different media. Toy manufactures have opportunities for product managers, accountants, and marketers.

CABLE PATHWAYS

THE TASK

In this project, you will explore ways of providing network connections to computer stations in a given room. You will calculate the cost to install cable pathways and submit a bid for the contract.

Suggested Group Size: 3

Materials: Grid paper; a computer with spreadsheet programs, Internet access (optional)

BACKGROUND

Many businesses and schools install computer stations as part of new buildings, or as the result of renovations. Since most computers work as part of a network, the rooms in which they are placed must allow for cable pathways. Cables may be enclosed to protect them.

Suppose you have a business that specializes in the installation of enclosed cable systems and you wish to bid on the installation of an enclosed cable system for the room shown on page 150. Assume the cable system will be installed in a space beneath the floor and you have free access to put the system in any arrangement that you find efficient.

- What would be the first step in estimating how much to bid for the job?
- What information do you need to calculate the cost for your company to do the job?
- Why would cable systems be enclosed?
- What material do you think would be used to make the enclosure system? Research the types and cost of cable pathway support systems that are available in the marketplace.

SOURCE LINK

- If you wish to review the use of spreadsheets in financial transactions refer to the Source Book, Chapter 4: Personal Finance. For concepts of surface area and volume, see the Student Reference in the Source Book.

Inserting cable into SCSI port

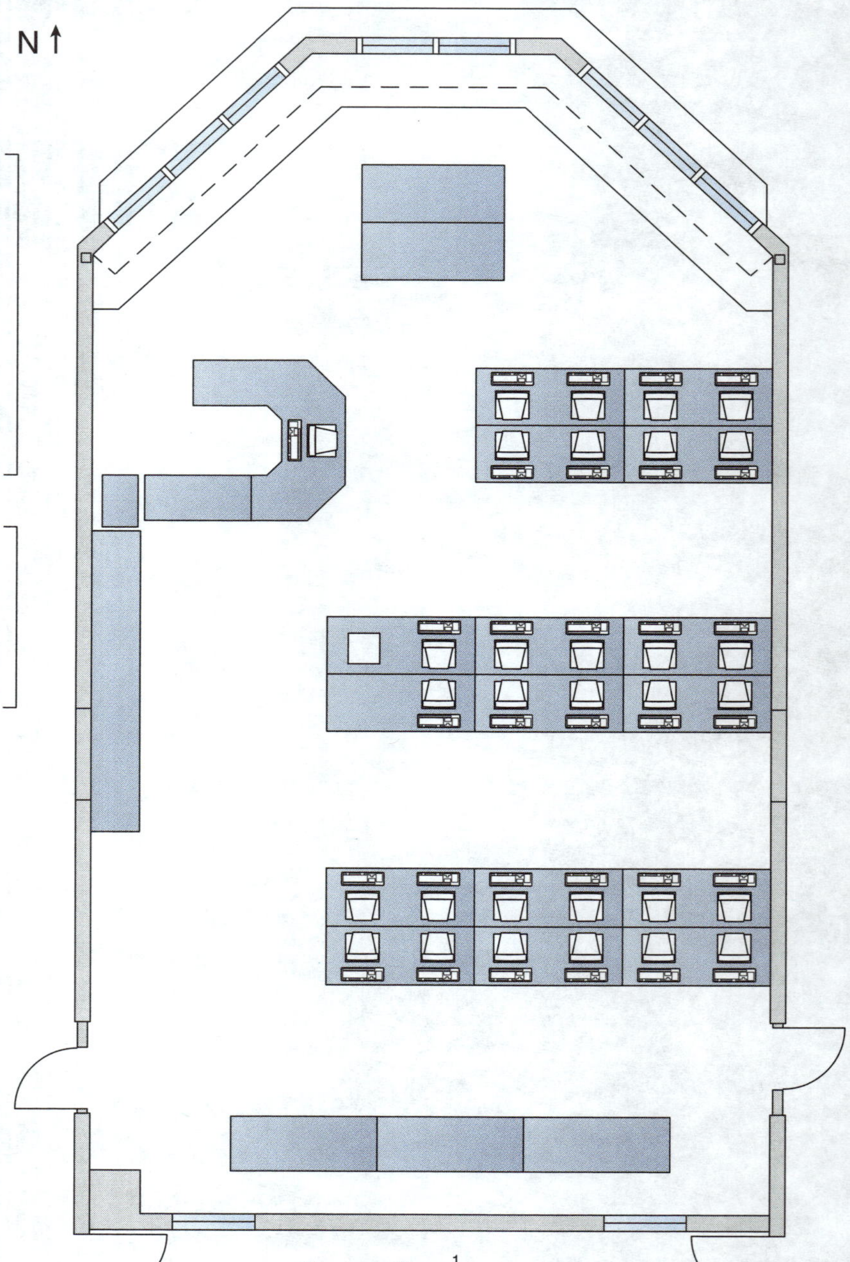

Scale 1:72 $\frac{1}{2}$ inch = 3 feet

GETTING STARTED

An accurate estimate of the cost of materials for a project is essential when a bid is prepared. Too low an estimate will result in no profit, or a loss, for the contractor. Too high an estimate will result in the loss of the contract and potential profits to a company with a lower, more realistic bid. The following questions involve estimates of costs of various materials used in cable enclosure systems.

1. The diagram shows a tin structure for enclosing a cable system. All the angles are right angles and the lengths are in decimetres. A special latex coating is applied to all outside surfaces. What does the coating cost, if latex costs 28¢/cm^2?

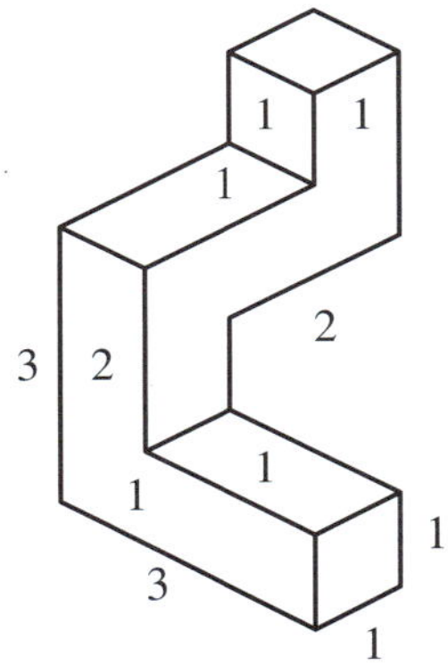

2. Computers in adjoining rooms are to be connected to each other and to the main network by a cable pathway as shown in the diagram. The cable runs in a space beneath the floor, 10 inches below the main floor. Beneath each computer station the cable enclosure system must rise to meet the floor above. Lidded, aluminum cable trays that cost $12.50 per foot support the cable pathway. Calculate the cost of the cable trays needed for this extension of the cable pathway.

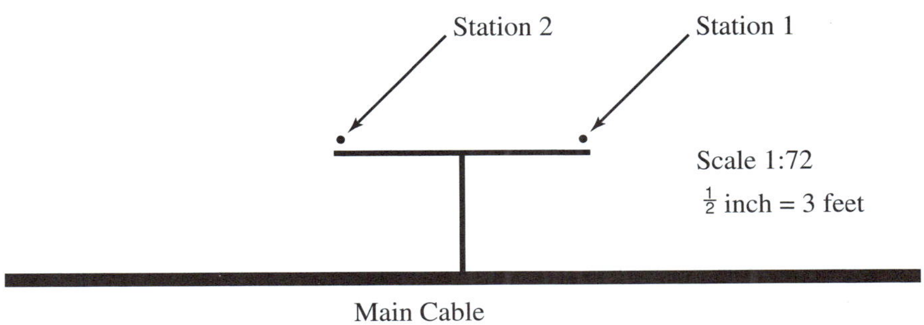

3. Tin plate for making cylindrical cans comes in sheets that are 240 cm by 160 cm and cost \$3.20 per sheet. Cans are 6 cm in diameter and 11 cm high and have 3 seals each. Seals cost 0.8¢ each to make. One sheet of tin plate is used to make pieces for ends and 2 sheets are used to make pieces for sides.

a) How many ends and how many sides can be made from the 3 sheets of tin plate?

b) How many cans can be made from the 3 sheets? What is the cost per can?

c) Is there a way to make more cans from the 3 sheets, or the same number of cans from less tin plate?

d) How much money is saved if you use the method devised in part c?

PROJECT PRESENTATION

In Getting Started, you calculated the cost of materials when given project specifications. Plan an enclosed cable system to provide connections at floor level for the room shown on page 150. Assume there is an existing cable that is accessible in the space beneath the floor along the full length of the south wall of the room. Assume the cable enclosure pathway will be 18 inches below the main floor level. Beneath each computer station, the cable enclosure system must rise to meet the floor above. This will require vertical and horizontal components. Use the diagram from exercise 1 as a guide.

Your completed project will include the following:

- A diagram of the planned cable system superimposed on the diagram of the room
- Calculations to show the cost of tin and latex coating for the system (assume tin plate is used, as in exercises 1 and 3)
- Calculations to show the cost of materials for the system (assume aluminum trays are used, as in exercise 2)
- Calculations to show the cost of materials for the system if an alternative support system is used

Work as a team to plan the least expensive cable enclosure system to reach each of the computers. Here is a detailed description of each person's responsibilities.

Journeyman Sheet Metal Worker: Find the cost of tin necessary to construct the system and the cost of latex coating to protect the system. Show all calculations in your estimate.

Researcher: Find the material cost if aluminum trays are used or if an alternative method of support is used. You may wish to use a spreadsheet to compare the costs for the different options.

Technical Draftsperson: Produce a scale drawing of the computer network and superimpose a top view of the least expensive cable enclosure system. For one of the banks of computers, create a front view to show how the system would be brought from beneath the floor to the surface level.

Career Opportunities

The building construction and renovation industries need people skilled in measurement, in estimation, and in costing of materials. Plans are drawn by designers and draftspeople. Business and budgeting skills are needed to bring a project to completion.

Ergonomic design

Suggested Group Size: 3

Materials: A large protractor, grid paper, a measuring tape

THE TASK

In this project, you will design a computer station that is comfortable and provides health benefits to the user. You will use ergonomic principles to ensure your station meets the requirements of a safe workplace, and cost the project within a budget.

BACKGROUND

To sit in one position for a long time is not healthy. People who work at computers often do exactly that. Maintaining one's position over time can create soreness and affect the body's circulation of fluids. A computer station that allows a worker to change position and yet continue to work will improve circulation, flexibility, and comfort for the worker.

Study the posture guidelines shown on page 156.

- What are some of the physical symptoms experienced by a person who remains in the same position for a long time? Where is soreness most likely to occur? Why?
- What types of jobs are likely to cause a worker to be stationary for long periods?
- What forces act on a person who sits at a typical work desk?
- What types of health problems might develop in workers whose jobs cause them to be stationary for long periods?
- What does "ergonomic" mean?
- What are the benefits of an ergonomically designed computer station, from an employer's perspective?

SOURCE LINK

- To review concepts of range and unit pricing, refer to the Student Reference in the Source Book.

0-60°
70°-135°
60°-90°
90°-120
0-35°
0-35°

Ergonomic design

Posture Guidelines

These guidelines apply to seated as well as standing postures.

Head/Neck:

Maximum: 30° of forward bending. (A)
Maximum: 20° twist from side to side. (B)

Elbows:

Work in 70–135° range, with keyboard tilted to match. (C)
Elbows should be relaxed near your torso.

Hand/Wrist:

Forearm, wrist, and hand should be fairly straight and not significantly bent in any direction. During keying, fingers should be slightly curved out but not curled.

Torso/Thigh:

90°–120° range. (D)

Thigh/Knee:

60—90° range. (E)

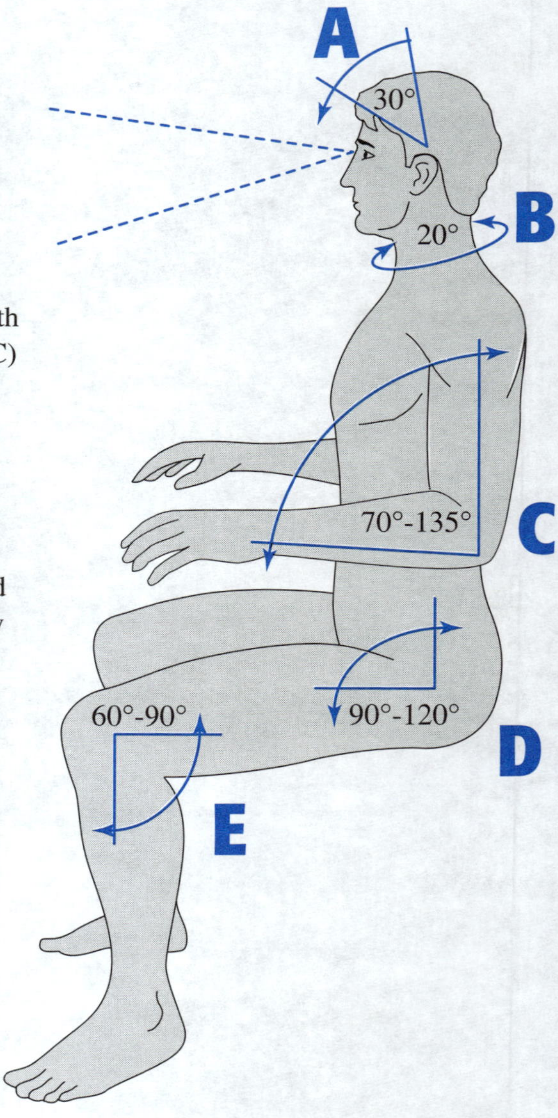

Shoulders:

1. No elevated or shrugged shoulders.
2. Arms not raised above your shoulder.
3. Elbows should rest close to your torso.
4. Make sure to provide support if elbows are not close to your torso.

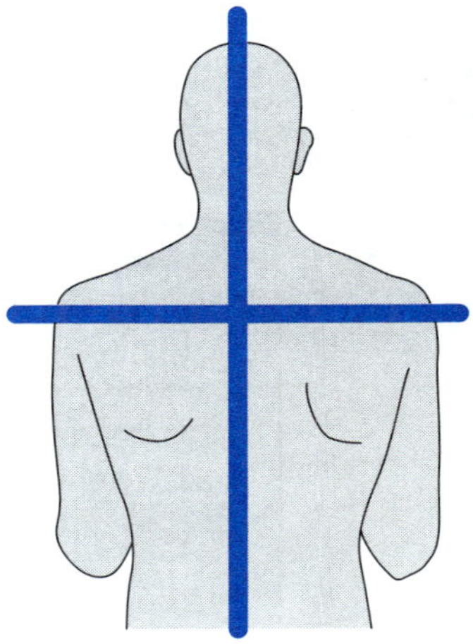

Primary work area

The area where you frequently perform tasks (e.g., typing, using the mouse) without overextending your upper body

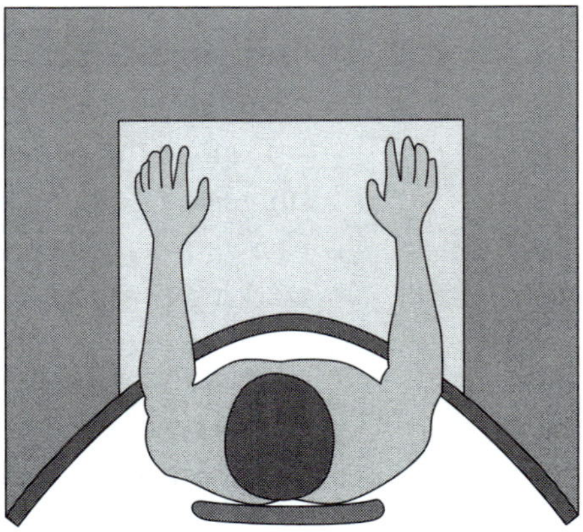

Visual Zone

The most frequently looked at objects

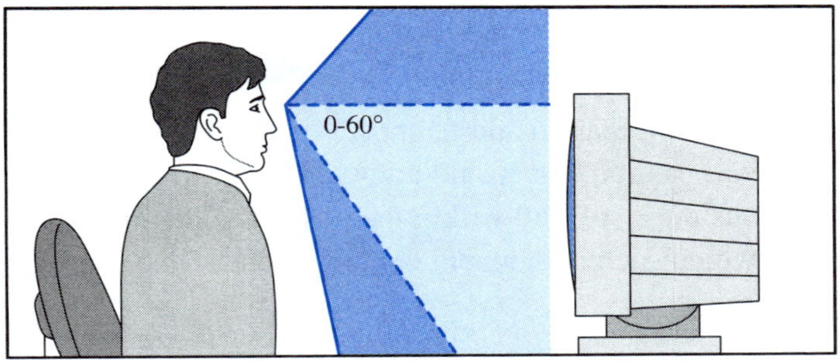

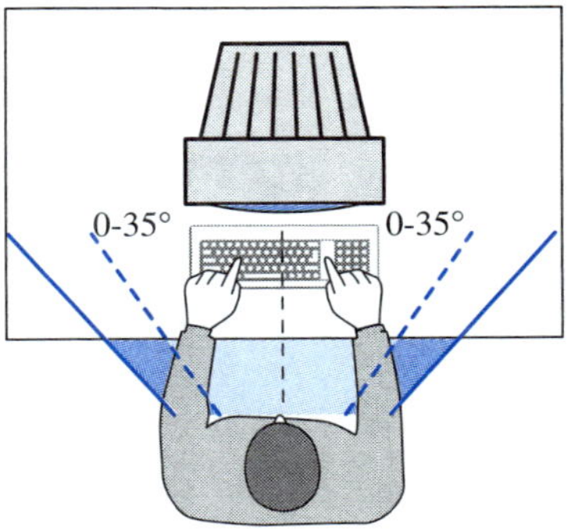

Adapted courtesy of 3M

Ergonomic design

GETTING STARTED

Gather data on the normal posture of a student working at a desk. Have 1 person assume a typical working posture and measure the following aspects. Use the diagrams supplied in Background as a guide.

Measure	Guideline	Subject
Head/Neck forward bend angle		
Head/Neck twist angle		
Elbow angle		
Hand/Wrist angle (should be near zero)		
Torso/Thigh angle		
Thigh/Knee angle		
Visual zone range		

1. Compare the measurements and decide if the student's regular working position would fall within the guidelines for healthy posture. If it does not, move the person so that his or her position does fall within the suggested guidelines. Draw a stick-figure diagram to represent the person. Use various views, such as top or side, to record his or her normal working position.

2. Extend the stick-figure diagrams to show how a chair could be built to support the person in a healthy posture. Include a headrest, elbow rest, torso rest, seat, thigh rest, and foot rest.

3. Assume the chair you designed is to be framed with $\frac{1}{2}$-inch tubing that costs $3 per foot. Estimate the length of tubing needed.

PROJECT PRESENTATION

Use the data collected in Getting Started and the posture guidelines found in Background to create a work station that would allow a worker to change position. Any new positions must still fall within the posture guidelines. Show the range through which each component can travel and still remain within the posture guidelines.

The following constraints apply to the development of the computer work station:

- Material costs must not exceed $150.
- Steel tubing costs $3 per foot.
- Upholstery costs $50 per chair.
- Adjustment pivots that allow parts of the chair to move cost $5 each.
- The computer monitor may be free standing, but the keyboard is attached to the arm rest of the work station.

Your completed project will include the following:

- Scale diagrams, including measurements, of side and front views to show a typical work position
- A list of the posture guidelines that led to the development of your work station
- Side and front views of the extremes of range of adjustment permitted by your work station
- The cost of materials for the system
- An advertising brochure for your creation

Here is a detailed description of each person's responsibilities.

Designers (2): Create side and front views of the work station. Show the worker in a reclining position to demonstrate how your work station differs from a regular office-type desk. One designer should draw the side view and the other should show the complementary front view.

Writer (1): Create a brochure to advertise the work station. Include reasons why such a station is needed and the advantages of your particular design. Include the designers' diagrams and details to show how the system works. Use a table or spreadsheet to present the cost projections for the materials needed.

Career Opportunities

An understanding of ergonomic principles and the importance of workplace design to employee health is needed by workers in industrial health and safety. Architects, planners, and furniture designers also must be aware of these principles.

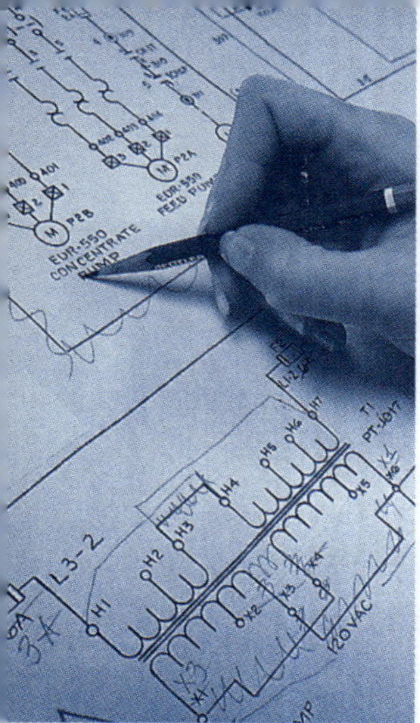

Designing
a storage tank

THE TASK

In this project, you will prepare a design and a budget estimate for the fabrication of a liquid storage vessel. You will work with dimensions, unit pricing, spreadsheets, and modelling to plan your vessel.

Suggested Group Size: 2

Materials: Paper, construction paper, ruler, tape, scissors; spreadsheet software program, *The Geometer's Sketchpad* or other dynamic geometry software, Tank Design sketch available on the *Teacher's Resource Book CD*-ROM (optional)

BACKGROUND

There is often a need for custom-made materials in modern industry. With the aid of technology, it is a simple matter to incorporate changes in design into production runs. Many vehicles manufactured today are custom made in response to orders from consumers and dealers.

Your team is asked to prepare a design, a scale model, and a cost estimate for the fabrication of a storage tank for liquids. You must consider costs for materials, fabrication, and painting.

Here are some aspects to consider before you begin.

- What characteristics does a good design have?
- How important is it to make fabrication as easy as possible?
- Is it better and cheaper to build a tank larger than the specified minimum or to cut materials to fit smaller dimensions and possibly increase waste material?
- Will any modifications be required for the storage of different types of liquid?

SOURCE LINK

- To review volume and surface area, look in the Student Reference. For help with *The Geometer's Sketchpad*, see Utility 23 (available from your teacher).

Petroleum Storage Tanks

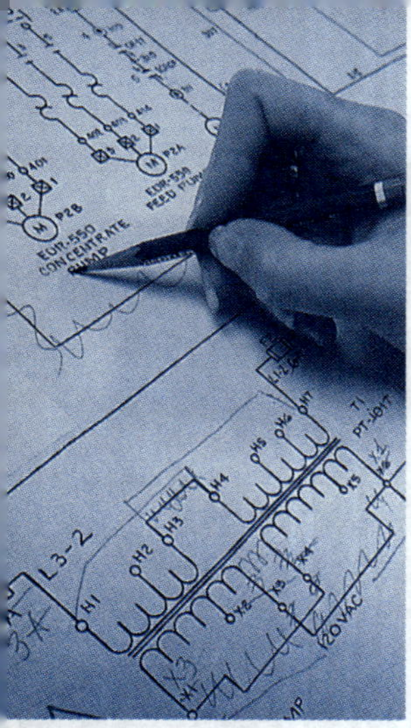

Designing
a storage tank

GETTING STARTED

The specifications for the liquid storage tank are as follows:

- Cylindrical, with horizontal axis
- Minimum capacity 4000 L
- Maximum length 3 m and maximum diameter 2 m
- Constructed from 4.7-mm stainless steel
- One 76-mm fill port on one end, centred 90 mm from the highest point on the circumference
- One 76-mm exit port on one end, centred 90 mm from the lowest point on the circumference
- One coat of primer and two coats of paint on exterior
- Markings on end of tank to indicate 500-L increments of liquid
- Budget of $600 for stainless steel

In your shop, you have access to material and cost information.

- 1 m^3 contains 1000 L.
- Steel comes in rolls of width 1.8 m, 2.1 m, or 2.4 m.
- The cost of steel varies, but for estimation purposes the cost is $30/$m^2$.
- Cutting and welding use shop time and materials, and cost about $1.50/m.
- Shop charges for miscellaneous work (painting, handling) are $45/h.
- Primer covers 9m^2/L and costs $6/L.
- Paint covers 7.5m^2/L and costs $8/L.
- Painting rate is about 50 m^2/h.
- Preparation for painting is about 20 m^2/h.
- Set up and clean up for each operation takes $\frac{1}{2}$ h of shop time.

1. Take a standard sheet of paper, roll it lengthwise, and tape the edges to make a cylinder. What is the volume of the cylinder you created? What area of paper would be needed to make the circular ends? How much paper would be used, including waste, if the ends were also cut from standard sheets?

2. Take another standard sheet of paper, roll it across the width, and tape the edges to make another cylinder. Determine the volume, area of ends, and amount of paper used, as in exercise 1. Which would be the better tank design, 1 or 2? Why? Which is easier to make?

3. In your tank design, you will need to specify dimensions of length and diameter. What dimensions and formulas are needed to determine each amount?

   a) volume or capacity **b)** material used

   c) cutting and welding to be done

4. Investigate options for the length and diameter of the tank. Set up a table as shown in Table 1 (or a spreadsheet) to determine and record options for length and diameter. All options must produce a tank with a volume equal to or greater than the minimum volume specified (4000 L), but the budget limitation of $600 for stainless steel must be met. Select one of the options for your design.

Table 1

Tank #	Length	Diameter	Circumference	Area Body	Area Ends	Total Area	Volume	Waste

The Geometer's Sketchpad sketch Tank Design, available from your teacher, may help you with the design process. An example is shown at the end of the project. This sketch allows you to adjust the dimensions of the tank by dragging the reference segments for tank radius, length, and fluid height. To calculate lengths, circumferences, areas, and volumes, use the **Measure** menu after you have selected the appropriate parts of the sketch.

5. To make your tank, you will need to cut and weld pieces from several sheets of steel. Prepare a supply of construction paper, box board, or file cards, cut to scale to represent the steel sheet stock you plan to use. Use this material to build a scale model of the tank design you chose in exercise 4. Note that you need to cut and tape (weld) pieces together to make the tank.

Designing
a storage tank

6. What are alternative ways to increase the volume of the tank, apart from welding on another piece to make the tank a little longer? Remember that each operation takes time and materials and these must be considered in your total cost estimate.

7. Prepare a spreadsheet to illustrate the cost breakdown for fabrication of your tank design, based on unit prices. Include material costs (steel, paint, and primer) and costs of operations (cutting, welding, painting).

8. The formula (with **Mode** on the calculator set to radians) for the volume of liquid in a horizontal cylindrical tank is:

$$V = \frac{D^2L}{4}\left[\cos^{-1}\left(\frac{D-2h}{D}\right) - \frac{D-2h}{D}\sqrt{1-\left(\frac{D-2h}{D}\right)^2}\right]$$

The variables are: V = volume, L = length, D = diameter, h = height of liquid.

Use a spreadsheet, calculator tables, or the Tank Design sketch from *The Geometer's Sketchpad*, to determine where to place end markings on your tank to indicate 500-L increments in volume. In your spreadsheet or calculator table, input values for diameter, length, and height. Adjust the values for height until the required volumes are determined. If you use *The Geometer's Sketchpad*, adjust the height of the fluid in the tank until the desired volume is reached, and note the height of the liquid at that point. Include the end markings on your model or diagram.

PROJECT PRESENTATION

Incorporate your rough work from Getting Started in your project. Your completed project will include the following:

- A memo to your supervisor that indicates the advantages of your design
- An invoice for the fabrication that shows a complete cost breakdown, with all costs itemized and total cost calculated
- A "blueprint" diagram for fabrication to illustrate how to cut and weld pieces
- A scale model made from construction paper or some other suitable material

Here is a detailed description of each person's responsibilities.

Designer: Oversee and/or complete the design portion of the project. Suggest options for sizes and use of materials, and prepare diagrams and models. Assist the Estimator to prepare the final memo to the supervisor.

Estimator: Work with the Designer to organize information from design options and assist in recommending the best design. Prepare the detailed costing spreadsheet and invoice, with input from the Designer. Coordinate the written memo to the supervisor.

Career Opportunities

Design and costing skills are needed in many areas, as shown by this practical project for a welding company. Design skills can lead to careers in graphic arts, construction planning, and architecture. Costing skills are used by estimators, insurance adjustors, and company planners.

Designing a Tank

radius = 2.24 cm
length = 7.12 cm
fluid height = 4.44 cm
Area segement = 15.71 cm^2
(Area segment)•length = 111.87 cm^3 = **liquid volume**
Circumference end = 14.06 cm
Area end = 15.73 cm^2
2•(Area end) + (Circumference end)•length = 131.57 cm^2 = **surface area**

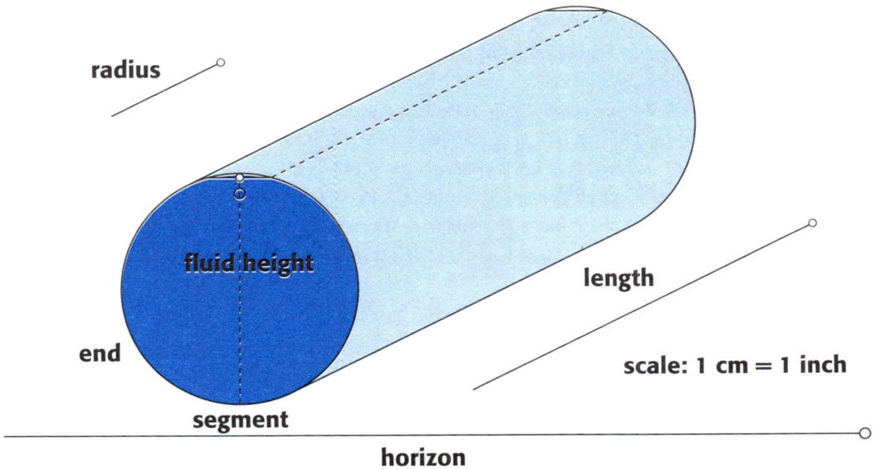

PHOTO CREDITS AND ACKNOWLEDGMENTS

The publisher wishes to thank the following sources for photographs, illustrations, articles, and other materials used in this book. Care has been taken to determine and locate ownership of copyright material used in the text. We will gladly receive information enabling us to rectify any errors or omissions in credits.

PHOTOS

Cover Montage - Dove: Sue Streeter/STONE; Hand and Rings: Phil Borges/STONE: **p.i** (top center) Sue Streeter/STONE; **p.iv** (center) Pictor International/Picture Quest; **p.iv** (center) Tony Stone Imaging/STONE; **p.v** (top left) Artbase Inc.; **p.vi** (center) Alain Masson/Firstlight.ca; **p.vi** (center) Jim Olive/Spectrum Stock; **p.2** (top left) Dave Starrett; **p.4** (top left) Dave Starrett; **p.5** (bottom left) Dave Starrett; **p.6** (top left) Dave Starrett; **p.7** (center right) 1999 Jason Laure'/Magdagascar; **p.8** (top left) Dave Starrett; **p.10** (top left) Pictor International/Picture Quest; **p.10-11** (background) Tony Stone Imaging/Stone**p.12** (top left) Pictor International/Picture Quest; **p.12** (center left) Dave Starrett; **p.12** (center right) Dave Starrett; **p.14** (top left) Pictor International/Picture Quest; **p.14** (top right) Dave Starrett; **p.16** (top left) Pictor International/Picture Quest; **p.18** (top left) Pictor International/Picture Quest; **p.20** (top left) Dave Starrett; **p.20-21** (top center) Barrett & MacKay Photo; **p.20-21** (background) Richard Shiell/Animals Animals Earth Scenes; **p.20-21** (top right) Tony Giammarino; **p.20-21** (top center) Barrett & McKay Photo; **p.22** (top left) Dave Starrett; **p.22** (bottom right) Artbase Inc.; **p.2-3** (background) Dave Starrett; **p.24** (top left) Dave Starrett; **p.26** (top left) Dave Starrett; **p.28** (top left) 1997 Jose L. Pelaez/Firstlight.ca; **p.28-29** (background) Artbase Inc.; **p.30** (top left) 1997 Jose L. Pelaez/Firstlight.ca; **p.30** (bottom left) Dave Starrett; **p.32** (top left) 1997 Jose L. Pelaez/Firstlight.ca; **p.33** (center left) Colin Garratt Milepost 92/MAGMA; **p.34** (top left) Dave Starrett; **p.34-35** (background) Images/Firstlight.ca; **p.35** (top right) Wei Yan/Masterfile; **p.36** (top left) Dave Starrett; **p.37** (center left) Ian Crysler; **p.38** (top left) Dave Starrett; **p.38** (center right) Artbase Inc.; **p.40** (top left) Peter Vadnai/FirstLight.ca; **p.40-41** (background) Artbase Inc.; **p.42** (top left) Peter Vadnai/FirstLight.ca; **p.44** (top left) Peter Vadnai/FirstLight.ca; **p.45** (top left) Dave Starrett; **p.46** (top left) Dave Starrett; **p.46-47** (center left) Ted Strensninsky/MAGMA; **p.47** (top right) Bettmann/CORBIS/MAGMA; **p.47** (bottom right) Antoni Mo/FPG; **p.48** (top left) Dave Starrett; **p.49** (bottom right) Dave Starrett; **p.50** (top left) Dave Starrett; **p.52** (top left) Artbase Inc.; **p.52-53** (top left) Artbase Inc.; **p.54** (top left) Artbase Inc.; **p.54** (bottom center) Alan Brooke/Masterfile; **p.56** (top left) Artbase Inc.; **p.57** (bottom center) Artbase Inc.; **p.58** (top left) Artbase Inc.; **p.60** (top left) Artbase Inc.; **p.60-61** (background) Gloria H. Chomica/Masterfile; **p.62** (top left) Artbase Inc.; **p.64** (top left) Artbase Inc.; **p.64** (center right) Artbase Inc.; **p.66** (top left) Artbase Inc.; **p.67** (bottom center) Tim Flach/STONE; **p.68** (top left) Artbase Inc.; **p.68-69** (bottom center) Tony Giammarino/GardenImage; **p.68-69** (bottom center) COMSTOCK/Grant Heilman; **p.70** (top left) Artbase Inc.; **p.72** (top left) Artbase Inc.; **p.73** (top left) Artbase Inc.; **p.74** (top left) Artbase Inc.; **p.74-75** (background) Thomas Kitchen/Firstlight.ca; **p.76** (top left) Artbase Inc.; **p.78** (top left) Artbase Inc.; **p.79** (top left) Greg Stott/Masterfile; **p.80** (top left) Scott Bennett/Spectrum Stock; **p.80-81** (background) Dallas & John Heaton/Stock Boston; **p.82** (top left) Scott Bennett/Spectrum Stock; **p.82** (bottom right) Norman Piluke/Spectrum Stock; **p.84** (top left) Scott Bennett/Spectrum Stock; **p.84** (bottom left) Jay Ireland & Georgienne E. Bradley; **p.85** (center right) David Austen/Stock Boston; **p.86** (top left) Bob Daemmrich/Stock Boston; **p.86-87** (bottom right) Artbase Inc.; **p.86-87** (background) Artbase Inc.; **p.88** (top left) Bob Daemmrich/Stock Boston; **p.89** (top right) John Sanford/Photo Network/Picture Quest; **p.90** (top left) Bob Daemmrich/Stock Boston; **p.92** (top left) Bob Daemmrich/Stock Boston; **p.94** (top left) Bob Daemmrich/Stock Boston; **p.96** (top left) Bob Daemmrich/Stock Boston; **p.98** (top left) Bob Daemmrich/Stock Boston; **p.100** (top left) Bettmann/CORBIS/MAGMA; **p.102** (top left) Bettmann/CORBIS/MAGMA; **p.104** (top left) Bettmann/CORBIS/MAGMA; **p.106** (top left) COMSTOCK/Bill Whittman; **p.106-107** (background) M & C Huot/Spectrum Stock; **p.107** (top right) Mark Burnett/Stock Boston; **p.108** (top left) COMSTOCK/Bill Whittman; **p.108** (bottom left) Mark Newman/Spectrum Stock; **p.110** (top left) COMSTOCK/Bill Whittman; **p.111** (bottom left) Tom Walker/Boston Stock; **p.112** (top left) COMSTOCK/Bill Whittman; **p.113** (bottom right) Y. Momatiuk & J. Eastcott/Stock Boston; **p.113** (center) Barrett & MacKay Photo; **p.114** (top left) Dave Starrett; **p.116** (top left) Dave Starrett; **p.117** (bottom center) Lloyd Sutton/Masterfile; **p.118** (top left) Dave Starrett; **p.120** (top left) Yogi Inc./Corbis; **p.120-121** (background) Roger Ressmeyer/Magma; **p.122** (top left) Yogi Inc./Corbis; **p.124** (top left) Alain Masson/Firstlight.ca; **p.124-125** (background) Jim Olive/Spectrum Stock; **p.126** (top left) Alain Masson/Firstlight.ca; **p.126** (bottom left) Tom Pantages; **p.128** (top left) Alain Masson/Firstlight.ca; **p.128** (bottom) Cary Wolinsky/Stock Boston; **p.130** (top left) Pat Lam/Spectrum Stock; **p.130-131** (background) Rick Fisher/Masterfile; **p.132** (top left) Pat Lam/Spectrum Stock; **p.134** (top left) Pat Lam/Spectrum Stock; **p.136** (top left) COMSTOCK; **p.138** (top left) COMSTOCK; **p.140** (top left) COMSTOCK; **p.142** (top left) Paul Eckhoff/Masterfile; **p.142** (bottom center) TRIP/H.Rogers; **p.142-143** (background) Bryce Flynn/Stock Boston; **p.144** (top left) Paul Eckhoff/Masterfile; **p.146** (top left) Paul Eckhoff/Masterfile; **p.148** (top left) Artbase Inc.; **p.150** (top left) Artbase Inc.; **p.152** (top left) Artbase Inc. **p.154** (top left) Artbase Inc.; **p.156** (top left) Artbase Inc.; **p.158** (top left) Artbase Inc.; **p.160** (top left) Richard Pasley/Stock Boston; **p.160-161** (background) R. Ian Llyod/Masterfile; **p.162** (top left) Richard Pasley/Stock Boston; **p.164** (top left) Richard Pasley/Stock Boston;

ILLUSTRATIONS

Artbase Inc. 148-149 (background); Bernadette Lau 25 (bottom right), Lau 26 (center right)

Bernadette Lau 26 (center right); Dave McKay 88 (center), 88 (bottom center), 89 (bottom right), 91 (bottom center), 93 (center); Greg Stevenson 115 (center), 119 (bottom center), 137 (center),155 (center): Jack McMaster 71 (center), 127 (center); Jane Whitney 138 (center), 139 (center), 139 (bottom right), 140 (center), 145 (center), 150 (center); Jun Park 128 (center), 156 (center right), 157 (top right), 157 (center right), 157 (bottom right), 157 (bottom left)